FEELING GOOD THERAPY:

THE 7 MOST EFFECTIVE STRATEGIES TO

MANAGE ANXIETY, FIGHT PESSIMISM, INCREASE

SELF-ESTEEM, OVERCOME OTHER MOOD

DISORDERS, AND HELP YOU DEVELOP

A POSITIVE OUTLOOK ON LIFE.

DWAYNE J. CURE'

TABLE OF CONTENTS

INTRODUCTION...1

STRATEGY 1 UNDERSTAND THE CAUSES OF MOOD DISORDERS AND DEPRESSION 3

What Do Cbt Therapists Believe About Depression?..4

How To Fight It Without Medication 8

How To Overcome 8

1. Healthy Lifestyle Changes To Combat Depression..8

    Food..9

    Physical Fitness...10

    Environment...11

    Social Life..12

    Hobbies And Activities...13

STRATEGY 2 UNDERSTAND THE CAUSES THAT GENERATE ANXIETY 15

Strategies For Working Through Worry, Fear, And Anxiety 16

Strategy To Overcome 19

How To Overcome 19

2. Coping With Worrying..20

    Why Is It So Hard To Quit Worrying?...21

    Negative Beliefs About Worrying 21

    Positive Beliefs About Worrying 21

    How To Quit Worrying 21

STRATEGY 3 UNDERSTAND THE CAUSES THAT GENERATE STRESS.............................25

3. Illnesses Caused By Stress 25

Insomnia..25

Depression..26

Disordered Eating And Eating Disorders...26

Panic Attacks And Anxiety..27

Viruses And Colds...28

Local Or Systemic Infections..28

Heart Problems..29

Cancer..29

Post-Traumatic Stress Disorder (PTSD)...30

Declutter Your Mind For Reducing Stress..30

The Role Of Habits In Reducing Stress And Mind Clutter..34

Strategy To Overcome..35

How To Overcome..35

4. Secret To Dealing Your Stress And Anxiety For Good 36

Turn Negative Thinking Into Positive Thinking...40

STRATEGY 4 HOW TO RECOGNIZE NEGATIVE THOUGHTS LEARN TO OVERCOME THEM
....43

Overcoming Negative Thoughts That Control Your Life..43

Recognizing Negative Thoughts...45

Identify The Trigger Thought Or Event...45

5. Decluttering Your Thoughts...45

Is Information Overload Serious?..46

Why Do We Experience Information Overload?..47

Information Overload Is Never Good..49

6. Challenge Your Thoughts Before Things Blow Out Of Proportion 50

How Healthy Thoughts Can Help 50

Take Time To Notice And Stop Your Thoughts 50

Learning To Choose Your Thoughts...52

How A Thought Journal Can Help..53

The Emotion Or Reaction You Gave 54

Identify The Physical Manifestation Of Your Emotion 55

Walk Away From Any Negative Thought Patterns 55

Become Aware...55

Practice Mindfulness Daily 55

Distinguishing Helpful From Unhelpful Thoughts 56

Strategies To Overcome..56

How To Overcome 57

STRATEGY 5 OVERCOMING THE ADDICTIVE RELATIONSHIP.......................................59

What Are Addictive Relationships 59

The Psychology Behind Addictive Relationships..60

The Dangers Associated With Harmfully Addictive Relationships 61

How To Overcome 62

STRATEGY 6 BUILD SELF-ESTEEM 63

What Is Self-Esteem? 63

What Is Confidence (Or Self-Confidence)?..64

Why Are These Traits So Important For Men & Women To Embrace, Develop & Strengthen?...............65

The Many Benefits Of Building Self-Esteem & Confidence..65

How To Get Started With Building Self-Esteem & Confidence Levels...66

A Self-Awareness Exercise: Get To Know Yourself & Your Restrictions 66

Strategies To Overcome Lack Of Self-Esteem 68

How To Overcome Lack Of Self-Esteem 68

STRATEGY 7 LEARN TO THINK LIKE AN OPTIMIST...69

Anger Management..71

7. Self-Healing.. 75

    Guided Meditation For Self-Healing 75

    Overcoming Death Anxiety 79

Changing Your Lifestyle To Regain Control Of Your Life 80

Action Plans 84

    Action Plan I – Dealing with Anxious Thoughts 84

    Action Plan II – Dealing With Avoidance.. 86

CONCLUSION.. 89

INDEX 91

INTRODUCTION

Living your best life and being your best self is more than just accomplishing all of your goals. It's also important that you can enjoy your life. After all, what's the point if you aren't even happy? There are a few ways that you can help you to **FEEL GOOD NOW**. It'll make your goals all seem worth it. You'll be able to be more positive and have a greater appreciation for life. Enjoying your life will allow you to see more clearly what matters to you and what life is all about. You'll feel free and creative. Of course, you can live your life and hate every moment of it. You can suffer through every day, not liking your life and wishing things were different. Or, you can take steps to make your life enjoyable for you so that you can make the most of it. Practicing gratitude can help you appreciate all that life offers truly, and you may feel more positive as a result. Appreciating yourself, those around you and everything that you encounter can give you some positivity. You may also learn how to focus on the present moment, allowing you to experience the greatest joy. You will live in the moment instead of dwelling on what happened in the past or what might happen in the future. Learning to do what you love can help you to be successful and happy. Often, we think that we can only choose one of these, yet it's important to remember that you can have it all. Finally, you'll learn about how and why to improve yourself constantly. If you remain the same, nothing will happen and you won't experience growth. Enjoying your life also requires you to enjoy change.

Practicing Gratitude

Taking a bit of time every day to practice gratitude can highly benefit you. It's super important to be grateful, thankful, and appreciative of all that life offers. When you practice gratitude, it's hard not to be a positive person. You'll be able to focus on everything that you have instead of everything that you want, which can have a huge impact on you. It'll be easier to find the positive traits of people in your life and to find positivity in everything that happens.

It's quite simple to practice gratitude. It's free, quick, and can even be fun. Just a few minutes a day can make a huge difference, and there are many ways to practice gratitude. You'll be a much more positive person for doing so, you'll feel better about your life, and you'll be much more motivated as well. Additionally, you may choose; however, you would like to practice gratitude. Because there are so many ways to do so, you may switch it up every day. You have many options to choose from, so there must be at least one that works for you.

You may keep a gratitude journal for yourself that you write in every day. You may have a gratitude list that you add to every day. This may even just be a portion of your journal. Simply writing down five things that you are grateful for each day can help you focus on what you love. This is great for the morning, as you can start your day on a positive note. You may also want to consider doing this before you go to bed so that you end the day thinking about what you were grateful for throughout the day. This can leave a better feeling about the day as a whole.

There is so much to appreciate! While outside, notice the beauty of the sky, plants, animals, and nature as a whole. Remember to appreciate your friends. They‘re the ones that are there for you and that you spend time with. The same is true for family. Before eating, take a small moment to be grateful for the food you have; not everyone gets a choice. Find the good in everything. Pause throughout the day and remember how great life is.

Express your gratitude. Tell others how much you love and appreciate them. Smile more often, especially at strangers; they‘re people too! Practice random acts of kindness without expecting anything in return. Call up friends and family just to say hello. Volunteer for causes that you‘re passionate about. Compliment others. Contact those who you haven‘t talked to in a while. Even spending time with others is a great way to express gratitude. Remember to appreciate the time you have with them. Thank those that serve you in your life. This could be a cashier, a janitor, or a flight attendant. These people are essential to the economy, yet they are rarely thanked for their work. You might make someone‘s day much better for it. Remember to express gratitude towards yourself. Be grateful for both your strengths and weaknesses, and remember to be grateful that you are alive.

It‘s also important to appreciate the challenges of life. It can be fairly easy to name all of the positive aspects of life you‘re grateful for. However, it‘s important also to remember to express gratitude for challenges and mistakes. They make you who you are.

STRATEGY 1

UNDERSTAND THE CAUSES OF

MOOD DISORDERS AND DEPRESSION

Depression isn't the same as a feeling of sadness. It's a mental illness with a specific set of symptoms that can only be formally diagnosed by a trained medical professional.

To qualify for a diagnosis of depression, you need to experience at least five of the following symptoms for a minimum period of two weeks. One of these symptoms must be either a depressed mood or loss of pleasure.

Symptoms: [xvii]

1. A depressed mood that lasts throughout the day, most days of the week

2. Loss of interest and pleasure regarding everyday activities, including previously enjoyed hobbies

3. Significant (5 %+) and unintentional weight change

4. Difficulty getting to sleep or sleeping too much

5. Feelings of restlessness or feeling slowed down

6. Loss of energy and fatigue

7. Feelings of excessive, inappropriate guilt and rumination over actual or perceived mistakes

8. Trouble thinking clearly, problems making decisions, or finding it hard to concentrate

9. Thoughts of death, suicide, or suicide ideation

Caution!

If you suspect you have depression, or are having thoughts of self-harm or suicide, you need to reach out to a doctor or therapist as soon as possible. Self-help guides can be very helpful, but they aren't a substitute for urgent medical care. You can always come back to this chapter when you have received a diagnosis and have started treatment as per your doctor's recommendations.

What Do Cbt Therapists Believe About Depression?

As you know, CBT is based on the idea that the way we see the world affects our mood and behavior. But how exactly can your thought patterns lead to depression?

Key Concept #1: Self-Schemas

A schema is a set of beliefs and expectations about a person, thing, or scenario. We have schemas about everything.[xviii] For example, most of us have a restaurant schema. Your ideas about going out for a meal in a restaurant include expectations about menus, tables, chairs, servers, food, drinks, and so on.

Although every restaurant has its décor, staff, and food, the basic principles are the same. If you've been to a few restaurants, you have a good idea of what to expect the next time. Schemas are useful because they help us plan ahead and respond to new environments. They help us understand how to behave appropriately around other people.

Just as you have a restaurant schema, you also have a —self-schema. ‖ As you may have guessed, a self schema is a set of beliefs about who you are and how you should act.

Someone with a positive self-schema knows they aren't perfect, but they usually think of themselves as a good human being. On the other hand, people with depression often have negative self-schemas.

If you have a negative self-schema, you may have the following beliefs:

—I'm just not good enough. ‖

—I'll never be successful, and I'll never get anywhere in life. ‖

—Everyone leaves me, and I'll be lonely forever. ‖

Beck thought that difficult childhood events could lead to a negative self-schema. For example, if a young boy is bullied at school for a long time, he may grow into a man who believes everyone hates him.

If you think poorly of yourself, you will be vulnerable to depression. A negative self-schema makes it hard to appreciate your achievements and enjoy relationships because you never quite believe you deserve them. Even when things are going well, you might find it hard to trust other people.

Exercise: Completing Sentences

Sentence completion exercises can help you uncover the negative self-schemas that are holding you back.

In your notebook, complete the following sentences. Don't overthink this. Write the first thing that comes to mind.

—I am the sort of person who… ‖

—In my experience, the world is… ‖

—When I think of the future, I think… ‖

This exercise can be quite illuminating. You might be shocked to discover just how negative your thoughts have become.

Your negative self-schemas might keep you trapped inside a cycle of negative thoughts and behaviors. For instance, if you always think that the future is bleak and that things will never get better, you might not bother to make plans or work toward goals.

Key Concept #2: Faulty Processing & Logical Errors

Negative self-schemas go hand-in-hand with logical errors. Logical errors are self-defeating patterns that keep you trapped in an unhealthy state of mind.

Here are a few of the most common logical errors, also known as —cognitive distortions: ‖ [xix] [xx]

1. Black and white thinking

When we're depressed, we often lose sight that life is neither perfect nor terrible. Instead, we are quick to judge things and people as —bad ‖ or —good, ‖ including ourselves. Also known as polarized thinking, black and white thinking keeps you from appreciating the nuances of everyday life.

2. Overgeneralizing

If you tend to overgeneralize, you focus on one poor outcome or event and decide that it's bound to happen again. You assume that a single setback dooms you to a miserable future.

For example, let's say you give a presentation at work. It doesn't go very well. Your boss pulls you to one side and gives you advice on how to improve next time.

A non-depressed person might be a little down or disappointed for a while, but they would probably act on their boss' feedback and even thank them for it. However, someone with depression might assume that all their future presentations are doomed and that their whole professional future is in serious jeopardy because of their poor performance.

3. Fallacy of change

Most of us are guilty of trying to get other people to change. Unfortunately, expecting others to change just to suit your agenda will make everyone unhappy. If you are stuck in this cognitive distortion, you believe that everything in your life will be better if the rest of the world gives in to your demands.

For example, a man might believe that his marriage and life in general will improve if and when his wife joins a gym, works out more, and loses the weight she gained after they got married.

4. Just reward fallacy (or —Heaven's reward fallacy ‖)

As we all know, life isn't fair. However, that doesn't keep us from feeling resentful when things don't go our way. Many people with depression think that if they do everything right and treat others properly, they will somehow be rewarded.

Unfortunately, if you hold this view, you'll be disappointed over and over again. Healthy people know that it's great to try your best, but we don't always have control over the outcome. Other people may treat us well or poorly, and we cannot control their actions.

5. Emotional reasoning

When you're in the grip of intense emotion, logical reasoning can fly out of the window. For example, if something makes you feel upset or scared, you might leap to the conclusion that it must be bad. For example, if a depressed person is nervous about going on a date, they might assume that this means it will go wrong and they probably shouldn't go at all.

6. —Should ‖

People with depression often use the word —should ‖ a lot, both about themselves and others.

Even if you don't try to tell everyone else what to do, —shoulding ‖ yourself isn't much better. Beating yourself up for not living up to a set of unrealistic or arbitrary standards will keep you locked in a state of self-criticism and depression.

7. Personalization

When you personalize an outcome, you assume that you caused it, even if you have no evidence. For example, suppose that your partner didn't get the promotion they wanted. If your first thought is, —If I'd been nicer lately and less stressed, they would have gotten it, I'm a terrible person! ‖ or something similar, that's personalization. When we're depressed, it feels as though we can't do anything right. Worse, it seems like everything is our fault.

8. Catastrophizing

Also known as —blowing everything out of proportion‖ or —making mountains out of molehills,‖ catastrophizing involves giving negative events or outcomes more weight than they deserve. When you catastrophize, you conjure up worst-case scenarios, usually in a matter of seconds.

For example, suppose you forget to pick up your partner's suit from the dry cleaner on your way home from work, and only remember once you start cooking dinner. If you are a catastrophizer, you may tell yourself things like, —I'm such an awful partner! We'll get into a fight, they'll leave me, and then I'll be alone forever! ‖

9. Filtering

When someone is overly optimistic about something, we say that they're wearing rose-colored glasses. If you're depressed, you're wearing gray-tinted glasses instead! If you focus on unpleasant details and ignore the bigger picture, you are filtering.

10. Blaming

People with depression assume that others have the power to —make‖ them feel a particular way. But this is a fallacy.

Suppose someone insults you. You might feel mildly offended, baffled, outraged, deeply upset, or something else entirely. What determines how you feel? Your approach to the situation. When you blame someone else for your emotional state, you are surrendering your power.

11. Mind reading

Do you assume that you —just know ‖ what someone else is thinking? Do you think you can tell when others are judging you? Mind reading can make you feel depressed, fast. For example, if you tell yourself, —Oh, so-and-so didn't return my email, she must think I'm completely incompetent and is avoiding me, ‖ there's a good chance you'll feel bad.

Depressed people are quick to assume that everyone is thinking the worst of them. In reality, most people go through their daily lives thinking only about themselves.

How To Fight It Without Medication

Having depression and all these negative outcomes is not the end to a happy life. The recovery will depend on the course of action you take, though the process is not as easy as you may want it to be. As you start the journey, it is good to note that whatever that seems so complicated can be the best remedy you might ever have! Therefore you don't have to fear trying things out.

The first step towards your recovery is accepting that you are depressed. You also need to understand the cause of your depression and the type of depression you may be having. So, how can you deal with depression?

Take care of yourself

Every healing process starts from you. Of course, the signs and symptoms that you observe may have been caused by some of your actions. The key here is to start diverting your attention away from depression and starting to think about other things that are refreshing. The change of approach will help you eliminate the threat depression is posing in your life.

You can start by setting achievable targets for yourself then working towards attaining bigger goals. The more —small ‖ goals you achieve, the higher the likelihood that you will feel better about yourself. Your goals should include such things like changing your lifestyle, taking a healthy diet, managing the stress levels, following a set schedule to carry out tasks etc. Approach your set goals one at a time spending a little moment appreciating your progress however small it is. Here is a quick summary of some of the goals that you could set to help you in dealing with depression.

How To Overcome

As you read through the list above, did any errors stand out for you? Note that you can be very depressed and only use one or two of these distortions, so don't be surprised if you didn't recognize most items on the list. Over the next few days, challenge yourself to spot your distortions.

1. Healthy Lifestyle Changes To Combat Depression

To ensure a healthy body and mind, you need to adopt a healthy lifestyle. You see, your lifestyle will be the backbone of everything else you do to overcome depression. If you do not fix it, you are unlikely to get any positive outcomes. Coping with depression will be easier if your lifestyle supports a healthy mind and body—because depression attacks the mind and body.

When we talk about lifestyle, what exactly do we mean?

A lifestyle is a way of life established by a society, culture, or an individual. There are elements of a lifestyle that define how you live your life. They include:

- Fitness: Your level of physical fitness and your involvement in physical activities.

- Food: How and when you eat and what you eat.

- Environment: Whom or what is around you, your experience of nature/the world around you, and your impact on it.

- Social life: The state of your social interactions and social fulfillment in areas such as friendship, relationships, community, and family.

- Hobbies and activities: Your pursuit of interests and hobbies. Which ones are they? How involved are you in them?

When we say make positive changes to your lifestyle, the above are the elements we have in mind. If any of them do not support a healthy mind or body, you ought to transform it.

Recommended lifestyle changes to help you overcome depression include:

Food

Eat healthy nutritious food; even though we may not understand this, we are what we eat. What we eat affects us physically, emotionally, and mentally too. Food affects how you feel, your mood, and how you think. Food is fuel, and therefore what you consume determines the kind of fuel powering your bodily system. If you fuel your body with low-quality oil, it will negatively affect its functionality.

For instance, sugar can cause mood fluctuations. You may notice that when you eat a sugary snack, you will experience a sudden spike in energy and positive emotions, what most refer to as a sugar rush. This rush has a very short life span, as a crushing low soon follows it, coupled with a sudden drop in energy and a rush of awful feelings. These energy and mood fluctuations make depression worse.

Experts also suggest that low levels of vitamins, low intake of fatty acids, and mineral deficiencies can lead to an altered mood and mimic mental health issues. In particular, insufficient vitamin D intake may lead to mood swings, lethargic feelings, and depression.

For reasons such as these, you need to consume healthy foods. That means you should consume more of:

- Complex carbohydrates such as whole grains and legumes.

- Fresh fruits and vegetables.

- Fatty acids (omega-3s and omega-6s) to be found in fish, nuts, and olive oil.

- Unsaturated fats such as olive oil.

- Enough water (at least two liters—about sixty-four ounces—a day).

- Amino acid–rich foods.

Limit/cut out the consumption of:

- Sugary drinks with empty calories, such as soda.

- Processed foods with little nutritional value.

- Caffeine.

- High-fat dairy.

- Fried foods.

When it comes to food and diet, the essential thing to keep in mind is to adopt a healthy, balanced diet.

Physical Fitness

The only way to achieve physical fitness is through exercise. Does this mean you should head to the gym and lift massive weights every day of the week? The answer is no. Taking that flight of stairs, parking a little farther from the office, or going for a morning or evening jog or walk counts as exercise.

According to experts, exercise increases the body's production of antidepressants. High-intensity activities such as jogging, running, step dancing, and others trigger the release of feel-good chemicals called endorphins and other hormones that make you feel happier.

Have you ever taken a walk around the block or gone to the gym for a hard workout while stressed? You may have noticed that afterward you seemed to have breathed out all that negativity, your stress reduced, and you were in a better mood.

How and when to exercise

When or how you exercise is entirely up to you. That mentioned, the recommendation is that you should develop a regular exercise routine considering your schedule and everything else on your plate. The exercise regimen must be sustainable and consistent; do not waste your time and energy starting something you cannot stick with—quitting halfway through will have no positive effect on your depression.

When you cannot get started

The physical manifestations of depression, such as reduced energy, disturbed sleep, irritability, and mood swings can result in a lack of motivation to exercise. Understandably, when you are feeling awful, waking up early and going for a jog or going to the gym is unfathomable. It is more comfortable to sleep in and wallow in your sadness. Learn to not listen to your body during such times.

Even when you are not feeling up to it, get up and start small: move a little! For instance, take a five-minute walk around the block, ride a bike, or skip rope for two minutes. The important thing is that you are doing something. Soon, five minutes will grow to ten, and then fifteen, until exercising becomes a big part of your morning routine. The more you exercise, the more you will want to do it because feel-good chemicals are addictive; you will want to feel that good every morning!

Environment

External factors also determine your mental well-being and mood. These factors are within our environment, which is why what is in your surroundings matters. When we talk about the state of your habitat, we are referring to the state of your workplace, your home, your favorite hangout spot, your neighborhood. The sounds, lights, voices, water, and the air around you matters.

Creating a healing environment

The natural environment

- Shield yourself against noise pollution: Trauma is enough noise in your mind. If your mind has to process and filter any more noise, finding peace and tranquility will prove elusive. Noise pollution acts as a parasite on the brain. During this time of healing, you must shield yourself from noise pollution. It is hard to do this if you frequent social places like clubs, marketplaces, malls, and so on.

- Increase exposure to natural lighting: Sunlight/natural light is naturally therapeutic. Experts recommend it as a way to deal with seasonal depression. Additionally, while giving us visual comfort, natural light/the sun is a source of vitamin D, which helps regulate our mood, energy, and mental clarity. We spend an average of eighteen hours a day indoors. Spend some time in the sunlight. If you cannot do so, perhaps because you have work, find a space near a window or move to a well-ventilated area that lets in light.

Work environment

A positive work environment is essential to your mental well-being. If your work environment is not favorable, then overcoming depression may be a little harder.

Work is more than a place where you earn a living. It should provide you an outlet for creative energy and education. Engage in a career you love, or create a positive work environment that gives you a chance to create a healthy work-life balance.

Home environment

Within your home, you are free to create a habitat that fosters your mental, emotional, and physical well-being and health. Try to have more human interactions, which are better for your health than TV and movies. Additionally, interact more with nature.

Social Life

Who is in your life? With which people do you spend most of your time? Where do you spend your time? How you answer these questions sums up your social life, which has a significant impact on your wellness and mental health.

You must maintain healthy relationships. If you keep the company of negative people, developing positive perspectives will prove difficult. If you are in toxic relationships, you will struggle to maintain a healthy mind since you will feel stressed and filled with negativity most of the time.

A healthy relationship is any relationship that has a positive impact on your life positively; such a relationship has mutual respect, love, and understanding. While in such a relationship, you can be yourself, grow at your pace, and you feel respected—and know that you are. Such a relationship is also free from verbal, physical, or emotional abuse and harmful elements like name-calling, hitting, or feeling forced to do unhealthy things.

Create a healthy, balanced social life. Having a social life does not mean you should be friends with everyone or attend every social gathering. Too many social commitments are not ideal for your mental health because they will leave you feeling pulled in too many directions, which will make it challenging to experience peace of mind and sanity. When you continue to put yourself under such pressure, overcoming depression and anxiety will seem too monumental an undertaking.

A healthy social life allows you to have time for yourself to tend to your commitments, quality time to spend with your family, time for your career, and time for your friends.

Limit your social media consumption. We now have a new social life on social media. You want to spend less time on social media, especially when you are dealing with depression. Using social media excessively can lead to negative emotions such as anger, envy, and bitterness.

Most social media posts have an element of showing off; everyone is posting their good moments. On social media, when you are feeling sad about your life, someone else is posting his or her glamorous and super exciting moments, which, even though they may not be 100 percent authentic, will leave you feeling desolate and as if your life is duller than it is.

Hobbies And Activities

Depression may cause you to lose interest in hobbies and activities you may have loved participating in early. If you have activities that made you feel happy and alive, you need to get back to doing them.

Enjoy your hobbies and commit to taking part in the activities you love. At first, you will not want to do it; this does not mean you should sit by the sidelines when you would genuinely enjoy a game of football or experimenting with a new recipe.

DWAYNE J. CURE'

STRATEGY 2

UNDERSTAND THE CAUSES THAT

GENERATE ANXIETY

ANXIETY AND YOUR BRAIN

Imagine you're enjoying a nice walk through the woods when you encounter a slithery thing on the ground. Light that's reflected off the object will enter your eyes and fall on your retinas, leading to signals that travel through the brain's relay station (the thalamus) and into the primary visual areas located at the back of your brain. The information is then relayed to other parts of the brain, including memory areas that match the object with the concept —snake. ‖

The fact that you're seeing a snake is then passed along to other areas, including the amygdala, tucked deep inside your brain, central to feeling and expressing fear and other emotions. How does your brain know to fear a snake next to your foot on the ground but not the one behind the glass at the zoo? The amygdala also gets input from the hippocampus, which is crucial for understanding context. Thanks to your hippocampus you may even start to feel afraid the next time you walk through the woods, even if you don't run into a snake.

Signals from the amygdala then activate a brain area called the hypothalamus, which will activate the fight-or-flight response of the sympathetic nervous system by releasing stress hormones like epinephrine (adrenaline). The hypothalamus also triggers the pituitary gland to release hormones into your bloodstream that travel to your adrenal glands (which sit on top of your kidneys), causing them to release additional stress hormones like cortisol. Our existence on this planet has depended on this coordinated response, allowing us to recognize and respond to threats, like moving away from the snake.

Just as it's important for our survival to learn to fear certain stimuli, it is also adaptive to learn when danger is minimal so we're not overly fearful. This new learning depends on providing our brains with new information, which anxiety-driven avoidance can prevent. For example, if I always avoid dogs because a big dog knocked me down when I was a little kid, I'll never learn that my early encounter won't be my typical experience with dogs. When we practice mindfulness and cognitive behavioral techniques for dealing with fear and anxiety, we retrain these brain areas to change their response to things that scare us.

Strategies For Working Through Worry, Fear, And Anxiety

There are many tools for managing overwhelming worry, fear, and anxiety, including cognitive, behavioral, and mindfulness techniques.

THINK (COGNITIVE)

When our fear is activated, we‘re likely to have thoughts that terrify us even more. For example, if we‘re gripped by fear on a plane, we might become convinced the plane will crash, which further heightens our fear and continues the cycle (refer to the CBT model of anxiety here). By challenging our anxious thoughts, we can interrupt this feedback loop.

A note of caution: when we‘re overwhelmed with anxiety, it‘s difficult or even impossible to talk ourselves down with reason alone. These techniques will tend to be most effective before anxiety has taken over and combined with behavioral and mindfulness techniques.

Remember that anxiety is not dangerous. We often come to fear anxiety itself, believing it‘s dangerous to be too anxious. However, as uncomfortable as it can be, anxiety itself is not harmful. Furthermore, fear about being anxious only leads to more anxiety. Keep in mind even in a severe bout of anxiety that the physical, mental, and emotional symptoms will not hurt you.

Reassess the likelihood of danger. Our fear will convince us that what we‘re afraid of is going to happen. But keep in mind that anxiety disorders by definition involve unrealistic fears given the actual risk, so the probability that they will come true is quite low. If your fear is telling you something really bad is likely to happen, you can use the Core Belief form to test this belief. How strong is the evidence supporting it? Is there any evidence against it? Has it happened before, and if so, with what frequency? If you discover any errors in your thinking, reevaluate the likelihood that what you fear will happen in light of the evidence.

Reassess the severity of threat. Sometimes the thinking error we make isn‘t about how likely a negative outcome is but how bad it would be. For example, Joe thought it would be terrible if people knew he was anxious while giving a talk. As he examined this thought, he realized that people might indeed know he was anxious from the quiver in his voice or shaking hands, but realized it probably wouldn‘t be a big deal. After all, he‘d heard speakers who seemed nervous before, and their anxiety hadn‘t colored his overall perception of the person or the quality of his or her speech.

Why worry? Worrying is a hard habit to break, especially because we often believe we should worry. We might tell ourselves that worrying:

- Helps us think of solutions to a problem

- Prevents us from being blindsided by bad news

- Shows we care

- Can make things turn out well

- Helps motivate us

These beliefs generally are false. For example, we can't avoid potential pain by imagining the worst-case scenario, which would be just as upsetting if it happened—plus we feel needless distress from countless worries that never materialize. When we see the futility of worry, we're more likely to redirect our thoughts.

Test your predictions. This technique sits at the intersection of cognitive and behavioral approaches. When you've identified a fear about how a specific situation will turn out, you can design a way to see if your forecast was right.

Lily dealt with a lot of social anxiety at work. She was convinced that if she spoke up in a meeting, her colleagues would ignore her ideas and probably even criticize them. She wrote down these and other expected outcomes before a meeting, and then she took a risk and volunteered her thoughts. While people seemed a bit surprised when she spoke up, nobody criticized her ideas. Her supervisor asked her to lead a subgroup that would develop her proposal. After the meeting, Lily wrote down the actual outcome versus her prediction.

Our core beliefs can distort our memories, thereby reinforcing our beliefs. It's important to record when our predictions turn out to be false, to help us encode and remember information that's counter to our expectations.

ACT (BEHAVIORAL)

When we change how we respond to situations that make us anxious, we can learn new behaviors that lessen our fear. Let's review some strategies for using our actions to combat our anxiety.

Approach what you fear. Facing our fears head-on is called —exposure therapy‖ in CBT and is the antidote to the avoidance that maintains anxiety. (This assumes, of course, that what we fear is not very risky; facing a dog that bites won't fix our phobia of animals, for example.) Exposure to the things that scare us decreases our anxiety by:

- Allowing our nervous system to learn that the danger is exaggerated

- Giving us confidence that we can face our fears without being overwhelmed

- Reinforcing our awareness that anxiety is not dangerous

Face your physical manifestations of fear. Anxiety about our anxiety can present an additional challenge. Panic disorder in particular can feature a fear of the panic-related physical sensations. For example, a person might avoid running because the resulting shortness of breath and pounding heart are similar to panic. Avoiding physical sensations only strengthens our fear and makes us more sensitive to the sensations. Exposure therapy can decrease our fear of physical anxiety symptoms. For example, we can do jumping jacks to cause breathlessness, spin in a chair to induce dizziness, or wear warm clothes to make ourselves sweat. Doing these kinds of things repeatedly lessens our fear of the physical sensations.

Let go of safety behaviors. When we have to do something that scares us, we often incorporate behaviors intended to prevent what we're afraid of from happening. For example, if we're afraid of going blank while giving a talk, we might write out and read our whole presentation. Other examples include:

- Keeping our hands in our pockets in social situations in case our hands shake

- Being overly cautious to avoid offending anyone

- Traveling with a companion only because of anxiety

- Triple-checking an e-mail for mistakes before sending it

There are two main problems with safety behaviors. First, they teach us that but for the safety behavior, things would have turned out badly, thus perpetuating the behaviors and our fears. Second, they can impair our performance, as when a capable speaker is overly reliant on notes, which prevents him from engaging with the audience.

In reality, many of our safety behaviors are useless, but we never realize it if we always use them (just like a superstitious practice we're afraid to let go of). We can combine testing our predictions with dropping safety behaviors to test whether they're necessary directly.

Strategy To Overcome

Breathing is characterized as a programmed capacity of the body that is overseen by the respiratory framework and ran by the central nervous system. Breathing can be seen as a reaction of the body when it is faced with pressure, where there is a stamped change in the breathing tempo and rates.

This is a piece of the body's fight or flight system and is a piece of the body's reaction to upsetting circumstances. People have been enabled to control their breathing patterns, and studies have proven that with our capacity to control our breathing patterns we can oversee and battle pressure and other wellbeing related conditions such as depression and anxiety.

Controlled breathing when utilized in the act of yoga, tai chi and other reflection exercises, is likewise used to achieve a condition of unwinding. Controlled breathing strategies can mitigate the accompanying conditions:

- Anxiety issues

- Panic attacks

- Chronic fatigue disorder

- Asthma assaults

- Severe agony

- High pulse

- Insomnia

- Stress

How To Overcome

Mindfulness provides several ways to manage our fears, through both the present focus and the acceptance components of the practice.

Train the breath. Our breath is closely connected to our anxiety: slow and even when we're at ease and fast and sharp when we're afraid. You can feel the contrast right now by first taking a series of fast, deep breaths in and out. Notice how you feel. Then breathe in slowly and out even more slowly. Feel the difference? When we're anxious we often aren't even aware that our breathing is mirroring our anxiety. Once we become more aware of the quality of our breath, we can practice more relaxed breathing:

1. Breathe in gently for a count of two.

2. Exhale slowly to a count of five.

3. Pause after you exhale for a three-count.

4. Repeat from step 1 for 5 to 10 minutes, one to two times per day.

These periods of focused attention on the breath will make it easier to practice relaxed breathing when you need it most. When you feel your anxiety start to increase, practice coming back to the breath.

Focus on the present. Anxiety grabs our attention and pulls it into the future. With practice, we can train the mind to come back to the present. As we disengage from future-oriented fears, we allow anxiety's grip to loosen.

2. Coping With Worrying

Worry is the interest you pay in advance for the loan you may never take out.

Do you always have to deal constantly with worries and anxiety? Here are some useful tips to help ease your anxiety and calm your troubled mind.

How much is too much?

It is very normal to experience worries, anxiety and doubts in daily life. It is our reaction to it which makes the greatest difference in our lives. It's very natural to get worked up about a first date, an upcoming interview, or an unpaid bill. Becoming frequently worried becomes overwhelming when it is uncontrollable and persistent. If every day you become worked up by picture all of the negative things that might happen to you, you are letting anxious thoughts interfere with your life and well-being.

Negative thoughts, incessant worrying, and constantly expecting poor outcomes will have a negative effect on your physical and emotional well-being. It gradually weakens you emotionally, taking your strength and leaving you restless and nervous, with headaches, insomnia, muscle tension and stomach problems.

The effect of this on your personal life, your concentration at school and work cannot be overemphasized. For some people, it's easier to take out their frustration on your loved ones and people closest to them, take alcohol or drugs or try to distract themselves by tuning out from everything.

Chronic anxiety and worry is a sign of Generalized Anxiety Disorder (GAD), a disorder that causes restlessness, nervousness and tension, together with a feeling of unease which can take over your life.

If you feel burdened by tension and worries, you can take a few steps to take your mind off anxious thoughts. Over time, worrying constantly becomes a problem. It becomes a mental habit when prolonged and is very difficult to break. Train your brain to be calm and think only positive thoughts, and change your outlook on life to a more relaxed and confident perspective.

Why Is It So Hard To Quit Worrying?

Worrying constantly does nothing but affect your life negatively. It keeps you up at bedtime and makes you edgy and tense in the daytime. You may detest the feeling of being nervous and confused, but it's very difficult to stop worrying. Beliefs about worrying, either positive or negative, fuel this nervousness further and may cause additional anxious thoughts in chronic worriers.

Negative Beliefs About Worrying

Most people believe that getting worried constantly is very harmful to your health and can drive you nuts. You may be worried about losing control over your thoughts and worries, fearing that they'll consume you and never stop. Negative beliefs about worrying may further fuel your anxiety, but positive beliefs about worrying can do as much harm.

Positive Beliefs About Worrying

You may believe, either consciously or unconsciously, that you can prevent bad things from happening to you, prepare for the worst and foster solutions. Probably, you keep convincing yourself that by worrying about a particular thing for a long time, you'll be able to figure it out eventually.

If you're convinced that getting worried is the most responsible thing to do in such a situation and the only way to avoid overlooking anything, it's even more difficult to break the habit. When you come to the realization that worrying is not the solution but the problem itself, you will be capable of gaining control of your mind.

How To Quit Worrying

Tip 1: Choose a Short Period Each Day to Worry

It can be quite difficult to be productive when your thoughts are consumed by worry and anxiety, distracting your attention from school, work, or your family. In this case, the strategy of putting off worrying can actually do a lot of good. Instead of getting rid of these thoughts, grant yourself permission to have these thoughts later on in your day.

Dedicate a period for worry each day. Set up a time and place to think of things that bother you. It should be at the same time every day (for example, 6 p.m. to 6:15 p.m. in the bedroom). Choosing a timeframe that won't affect your bedtime and or create additional anxiety in your life. During this period, you can worry about whatever you want. The rest of the day should be classified as worry-free.

Put down your worries in writing. When you find yourself thinking anxious or worrying thoughts, simply note them briefly and continue with your daily activities. Always remind yourself that there's time for you to think about it later; there is no need to get worked up about them now.

Tip 2: Challenge Anxious Thoughts

The way that you look at the world may be altered a bit if you are a chronic worrier and thinker. It changes everything, and you may tend to feel threatened. For instance, you picture only a worst-case scenario, and you assume the worst or handle your anxious thoughts as if they were facts.

As a result, you may not feel secure enough to tackle daily challenges head- on; you may assume that you'll lose it at the slightest sign of trouble. Such thoughts, also known as cognitive distortions, include: ―All-or-nothing ‖ thinking, having a blackand-white perspective, concluding that ―If it isn't perfect, then I'm a complete failure ‖ , or ―I wasn't hired for this job; I'll never get any job again ‖. You may make a generalization from just one negative experience and expect it to be true forever. Life doesn't work that way.

You may notice only the things that went wrong in your day, instead of things that went well, resulting in thoughts such as: ―I didn't get the last test question; I'm stupid, and I can't do anything right. ‖ . You may attribute positive events to sheer luck, rather than your own ability to create positive outcomes.

Tip 3: Differentiate the Solvable Worries from the Unsolvable Worries

Studies have shown that you experience less anxiety when you worry. While you think about the problem in your head, you're distracted from your emotions for a while and feel like you're actually solving a problem; in reality, getting worried and problem-solving are two different things altogether.

By problem-solving, you are examining a situation, thinking of solid ways to deal with it, and putting these plans into action. On the other hand, worrying seldom leads to any solutions. The more time that you spend thinking of worst-case scenarios, the less prepared that you are to handle them if they actually happen. That's the simple truth.

Is your worry solvable?

There are different types of worries; some have solutions, while others don't. Solvable worries are those that you can act to resolve instantly. For instance, when you're preoccupied with your debts, you can call a friend or relative to settle your debts, with the option to repay them later.

This type of worry can also be described as productive worry. On the other hand, those worries that do not have a corresponding action can be characterized as unsolvable problems; for instance, thoughts like: What if I get leukemia someday? What if my family gets involved in an accident?

In a situation where you can take action about the thing getting you worried, begin to look for solutions. Compile a list of all the ways you feel that you can solve your worry. Don't get caught in searching for the one perfect answer to the problem.

Concentrate on those things within your reach that can be changed instead of brooding over situations that are out of reach. After deciding upon the solution that will solve your problem, develop an action plan. Immediately you set out to address your fear; you will be less worried.

On the other hand, when the worry is not something you can solve, make peace with yourself by being at ease with the uncertainty. For people who worry excessively, many of their fears tend to be along these lines. People tend to worry when they are trying to anticipate the future, and this is done to feel more in control and prevent potential problems.

However, the bitter truth is that worrying doesn't solve anything; life is occasionally unpredictable. So why not enjoy your life now instead of being engrossed in unpleasant things that have not taken place?

Most people long for inner peace: the feeling that everything is, and will be, all right. But sometimes, we worry, develop fears, and ponder the same things over and over without finding a way out.

The tragic thing is that, of course, we know rationally that the upcoming test is not a life-and-death situation. Our child is probably not lying in the ditch just because he/she does not call at the agreed-upon time. Our dull headache is probably harmless and not the symptom of a brain tumor.

But when our anxiety rises, we think in circles or worry about failing, and we lose that realistic perspective. We are like under a "black cloud". Then we can only imagine all that has happened or is going to happen. We only see what is going wrong in our lives, family, company, and in the world. These thoughts are, in fact, only thoughts — but we lose our perspective.

Do you imagine disastrous, unpredictable things might occur? What is the possibility that these things will actually happen? Even when the probability that bad things will happen is low, do you still worry over the little chance that something terrible will occur?

Tune into your emotions and thoughts and observe them. You can overcome your worries by observing your feelings and thoughts while staying rooted in the present moment. Find out from your loved ones how they combat their uncertainty about things. Can you follow their strategies to overcome your worries?

Tip 4: Interrupt the Worry Cycle

Answer the following questions:

- What am I worried about?

- What possible solutions exist?

- Which solution should I choose?

- How and when do I implement the solution?

Just writing down your worries can provide you with some relief. If you then also write down different solutions, you will see your fears in a different light. You will adopt the observer perspective and will be able to think more logically about what you can do.

Meditate. Meditation helps to alleviate daily worries by shifting our attention. We focus only on the here and now and can leave the concerns of the past or future behind. Similarly, meditation can also help us observe ourselves and understand our negative thought patterns. We only need to find a comfortable, quiet place and focus carefully on our breathing. Various studies have shown that meditating not only helps to ease worries but can also reduce stress and anxiety.

Tip 5: Talk about your worries.

One way to worry less is to talk to our closest friends about what is bothering us. When we are worried, friends can help us to alleviate our fears and see things from a different perspective. They can help us to look at the problem from the outside. Then, we can often find a solution or come to realize that it's not as bad a problem as we feared. When they listen without judgment or criticism and pay attention to what we say, their empathy can help us to feel calmer and more relaxed.

Having someone listen to us with empathy is essential to make us feel better. Even professional help is very beneficial, in some cases, if you cannot find a way out yourself.

STRATEGY 3

UNDERSTAND THE CAUSES THAT

GENERATE STRESS

3. Illnesses Caused By Stress

Stress causes many kinds of illnesses that involve both the mind and the body.

You may be battling stress and have some of the health issues and diseases listed here:

Insomnia

Lack of sleep and insomnia exacerbates stress. Worry, uncertainty about the future, issues with your job, your relationships, your children, finances keeps a person awake at night. Some people are concerned with caring for a family member who is ill or a death in the family. Just navigating through each day can raise the level of stress. If stress remains uncontrolled, it interferes or delays the ability to fall asleep.

In order to battle against your lack of sleep that is stress-related, there are positive steps that can be taken. Reduce caffeine intake over the course of the day, stop watching TV or surfing on your computer at least an hour before bedtime, shut off all electronics when you're in your bedroom, and do not exercise prior to bedtime. A bedroom that is dimly lit, cool, and comfortable is the type of environment you want to have before you go to sleep.

Shut your mind off from the problems that elevate your stress while getting ready for bed. Instead, think peaceful thoughts, have soothing sounds or music programmed to play for an hour while you drift off to sleep. Prepare your mind for rest.

Violent or disturbing television programs can elevate stress and anxiety, especially in these days of mass shootings and the traumatic aftermath that people experience from these events.

Depression

Stress that remains unresolved can bring up emotions of anger or hopelessness in a person. Both of these emotions can lead to depression and have feelings prolonged.

Feeling chronically unhappy or sad, having trouble thinking with clarity, dealing with loneliness or feeling unloved and uncared for, or feeling shame or guilt, you are probably depressed, which often is related to excessive stress.

Illnesses you may have that are chronic may seem unrelated to depression. However, continuous daily coping with a chronic condition can be stressful and depressing.

A feeling of hopelessness sets in when a chronic condition is a day-to-day battle. The stress of maintaining the condition with medications, routines that can't be ignored, and the never-ending doctor appointments can be a stressful and depressing way to live.

Disordered Eating And Eating Disorders

When you're feeling stressed and overwhelmed with an issue that you just want to have gone away, do you find yourself looking for something to eat, most often that is tasty and sweet when these feelings well up?

Don't feel like you're alone. That's what many people do.

When people are stressed, they usually reach for a carbohydrate-laden food or a sweet treat to get a fast sugar rush. While your blood sugar may elevate for a short period giving you a false sense of energy, it will drop afterward, frequently making you feel sluggish and, sometimes, drowsy and slow.

There is another eating disorder that stress impacts and that is bulimia. Stress is thought to be an initiator for people who have bulimia and end up binge eating.

Chronic stress and stressful events are major causes of eating disorders. Some research has indicated that the overall pressure and stress for bulimics is more than two times greater than it is for normal women.

The stress may be expressed through anger, anxiety or depression, or physical decline and illness.

Try changing your eating habits when you get stressed out. Eat some crisp veggies like carrots or even raw green or red peppers that have a natural sweetness. Cut up an apple and eat a few slices. You can also pop some light butter popcorn. You'll feel fuller with fiber and stay healthy, as well. Don't allow your stress to have you make a bee-line to the cookie jar, your favorite Danish pastry or candy counter.

Panic Attacks And Anxiety

As with depression, disorders linked to anxiety and panic attacks often have a stress-related correlation.

Struggling with issues that cause you to feel ill-at-ease and have you experience extreme stress and that can manifest in fear and nervousness for reasons that are not clear.

Panic attacks and anxiety attacks are usually thought to be interchangeable. However, they are very different. Although they have some similar symptoms, there are differences that are distinct in how they manifest, how they are triggered, the length of time they last and how each is treated.

It is important to understand how different each attack is so your symptoms can be reported to your physician accurately. Their treatment is different.

The onset of an anxiety attack is different, whereas it is a gradual escalation of emotions. It is usually caused by a particular situation that can be targeted as the cause of the attack.

Symptoms of an anxiety attack before it occurs can be the feelings of worry, uneasiness, fearfulness or distress. These feelings usually begin before the actual attack and continue after the attack ends.

An anxiety attack can last longer than 10 minutes. If a certain situation is occurring that has caused the attack, the anxiety will continue until the situation changes or ends.

Panic attacks, on the other hand, come on instantaneously and spontaneously. This attack is instant. There is no gradual escalation, it just comes at any time, no matter what the situation. There is usually no identifiable reason why the attack occurred.

While you're experiencing the attack, you will experience crippling fear, as well as the fear of losing control. You also have a feeling of disassociation from your surroundings, known as derealization. You may also experience a detachment from yourself, known as depersonalization.

Panic attacks last, on average, approximately 10 minutes. After the attack ends, the symptoms dispel after the attack ends (Boring-Bray, 2018).

Physical symptoms for both attacks:

- Nausea

- Lightheadedness and/or dizziness

- Pains in the chest

- Difficulty in breathing

- Sweating

- Throat tightening or choking sensation

- Physical shaking or trembling

- Tingling or numbness

- Headache

If the panic attacks or uncontrolled anxiety attacks persist or accelerate in their occurrence, meeting with a psychologist or a counselor may be a step in the positive direction of dealing with the source of the issue.

Viruses And Colds

Illness of any kind can cause stress, even if the illness may be a common cold or virus. The immune system that is not functioning up -to-par and is being afflicted by stress will often get sick more frequently and quicker.

Alleviating stress can be helpful in regaining your health and healing from illness much faster.

Circulatory problems

Your body's veins and arteries can be made to tighten up due to stress and the response to the fight-or-flight feelings. Blood flow through the body can be compressed and create further problems such as poor circulation, blood clots or even a stroke.

Get a medical checkup and diagnosis about this type of medical issue.

Local Or Systemic Infections

Emotional or mental stress can delay or interrupt the physical healing of systemic infections, like food poisoning or local infections such as an infected toe/toenail or a splinter that goes unattended.

The body's positive energy is drained due to stress as it attempts to deal with worrying about stress-related problems. There isn't much left by way of energy to sustain the immune functions of the body to heal infectious injuries and illnesses.

Diabetes

Blood sugar that is out of control that is caused by stress is common in those who have diabetes. People diagnosed with diabetes need to eat and maintain a lifestyle that has to regulate their blood sugar levels in prescribed limits. Sugar levels increase or decrease based on the amount of stress a person with this disease is under.

People with diabetes who are overwhelmed and stressed need to monitor their blood sugar levels. If they're on mediation for type 2 diabetes, they need to take their medication, while type 1 diabetics need to monitor their insulin intake. Eating properly is also key to maintaining blood sugar levels.

Heart Problems

Your heart can palpitate, increase the pulse rate and have your blood pressure increase when you are stressed. Stress can put tremendous pressure on the heart and can damage it. Your blood cholesterol can increase by elevated stress levels. Monitor your blood pressure if you are under consistent stress to avert possible strain on the heart.

Exercise and proper eating habits can also help in reducing the stress levels that can affect your heart.

Cancer

Stress that is prolonged can cause chronic inflammation that contributes to cancer risk and exacerbates an already cancerous condition.

Although stress doesn't necessarily cause cancer in itself, all the other health problems that are linked with stress can cause the manifestation of cancer.

Overeating, smoking, and drinking alcohol in excess all can elevate the risk of developing cancer. These habits can develop and be stress-related.

Studies have shown that there are links between certain types of cancers and stress. The body's immune system is suppressed by stress; a person who is battling ongoing stress may not be able to fight against a major illness like cancer.

Other studies indicate that the recurrence of cancer can be affected by stress and fear of cancer returning. The production of the hormone cortisol occurs when the body is stressed for a period of time. This can inhibit the immune system of the body and make it more prone to the recurrence of cancer. (University of Rochester Medical Center, 2007)

New homeopathic treatments such as musical and relaxation therapy are now being included along with the medical treatments for cancer patients. These treatments can help to lessen and ward off the stress that the disease creates and reduce the side effects of the medical treatments prescribed that can be physically overwhelming.

Post-Traumatic Stress Disorder (PTSD)

This disorder develops in those who have had a trauma either directly or indirectly affect them. They suffer from functional impairment or distress for a period of time, usually a month at minimum and some who have been exposed to extreme trauma for the remainder of their lives.

The symptoms of PTSD include experiencing the traumatic again, evading reminders of the trauma, elevated anxiety and negative feelings or thoughts. Mass shootings, natural disasters, terrorist attacks and cities that are under siege have added to the burden of PTSD. Now global in scope and affects 4-6% of the world's populations, the major portion of traumas are associated with sexual or physical violence and accidents.

There is no known cure for PTSD and the treatments that are currently used to help those who suffer from trauma are not effective for all patients.

There is evidence that Vagus nerve stimulation (VNS) may be an aid that is beneficial when added to other exposure-based therapies. The Vagus nerve serves as a connection to the brain from the peripheral autonomic nervous system.

It communicates with the brain and sends a signal at times when heightened sympathetic activity is activated. The Vagus nerve counteracts the sympathetic nerve response. (McIntyre, 2018)

Declutter Your Mind For Reducing Stress

Clearing of the mental clutter is the only sustainable way to have a stress-free and meaningful life. When your mind can think clearly and make decisions based on priorities rather than instincts, your life becomes easier.

These days, the stress in life has increased so much that people have started thinking that peace is the goal of life, it isn't. Peace is the way of life and leading a meaningful and constructive life should be the goal. Even the animals and birds that do not have the same cognitive abilities lead a peaceful life. There is no reason for this life not to be peaceful or be chaotic until some external force is applied.

Think of young kids for that matter. They lead a peaceful and happy life. You need to apply force to make them unhappy. They are beaming with life. But, as we grow, we become gloomy, stressful, and sad. The person doesn't change. It is the clutter that gets accumulated in mind and brings the change in attitude.

If you closely look at the life of a child:

- A child has easy goals

- A child has clear priorities that bring happiness

- A child has easy decisions to make

- A child has few things to compete for

As you grow all these things change for you. You set unrealistic goals for yourself. Your priorities are complex and most of the times have no bearing in present. The number of choices in your life increase causing a lot of indecisiveness. This leads to anxiety, unhappiness, and stress. You increase the competition for yourself. Your mind starts raising the bar on its own. The more cluttered your mind is, the tougher your life will get.

The reason for most of our stress is unconscious decision taking. It is a result of a cluttered mind where decisions are mostly based on trends or instincts. Becoming mindful of our decision-making process and decluttering the mind can help in solving most of these problems.

We are more focused on living a full life rather than living a fulfilling life. We are running in a mindless race to gather material possessions not knowing their use or worth once we have gained them. We waste our lives running after success only to realize in the end that it wasn't worth the pain anyway.

We work for numerous hours in offices. We sacrifice our precious time in looking at the files and miss the smiles blooming on the lips of our toddlers. This is a great loss that can have no compensation in terms of monetary gains.

We bear great stress in form of responsibilities. We slog for endless hours in jobs, only to realize that we don't even have the necessary passion for the job. All these things increase stress in life. These are mindless activities are carried out without giving much thought.

This endless talk about not focusing on work and career entirely for money or searching for passion may look a little offbeat. To a materialistic mind, it is a bit off the track. However, it doesn't make the fact any less sad that we are ready to exchange happiness and joy in life in exchange for stress and worthless material possessions.

You work day and night to get rich. You have more than 1 home, more than 1 car and money that is only of any value to you in bank statements. But, you are skeptical to work for something that can give you real gratification.

If you think that searching for happiness in place of material wealth is a difficult and absurd phenomenon, then you are wrong. Not only a person but a whole nation has shown to the world that it is possible and holds merit.

Some major areas have a deep impact on your happiness. If things are neglected in these areas, they automatically lead to stress. Prioritize and see the things you want to have in these areas:

Health

While planning for life, most people never even give a fleeting glance at the health. While we are young, we take it for granted that we'll always be young, healthy, happy and energetic. This notion precipitates pretty fast and we have nothing else to do other than sulk. Health is one of the most important factors that affect our happiness and stress. If you are consciously planning for a stress-free life then leaving health out of that plan is unjust.

Chart out a definite plan for health and fitness. Decide the amount of time and effort you want to give to remain healthy.

Career

We spend the highest amount of time and energy at our workplace. We study, learn, and gain experience to have a stable and rewarding career. But, what use is a career that only keeps you aggravated and dissatisfied? It may give you the money, but that money is only good for boosting your ego and buying stress relievers.

A career should always be rewarding. Something that fuels your passion so that you can become more productive. Do not choose a career that makes you feel miserable. It will make you a part of the rat race.

Work is an important part of life. Yet, it is only a part of life and not the whole of it. If you start compromising with your life for work, in the end, you'll be left with very few things to remain happy. Your work life must have a balance. The amount of work you take must be based on the amount of work you can do. Succumbing to peer pressure, competition and greed may snatch away your happiness.

Relationship

Relationships are important as they complete us. They bring a sense of inclusion in life. However, expectations in relationships and especially unrealistic expectations can turn them toxic. Have a clear idea about the things you want in a relationship. Have a clear, frank and open dialogue about it while entering into a committed relationship. Be more open, accepting and inclusive.

Family

The family is something we easily push aside while making important decisions. The family has its place in life and it should be clear in your mind while you make your decisions.

Self-Improvement

The best thing about us human beings is that we have an indefinite potential for improvement. We can learn new things, languages, arts, craft and make ourselves better. Continuously work on making yourself better. Either it is developing your personality or learning new things, it will make you feel more satisfied. Nothing gives a greater sense of joy than the accomplishment of learning new things. It will keep stress low in your life.

Life Planning

Security is important in life to alleviate unnecessary stress. Planning for life reduces mental clutter. Things move in a more organized manner. You get more time to devote to yourself rather than worrying about the unknown contingencies. Plan things like budget, work, retirement, etc. well in advance.

Recreation

Enjoyment has a special place in life. It gives you joy and pleasure. The end goal of most of the above pursuits is to bring joy to your life ultimately. You must always have space for leisure in life. Plan recreational activities as you plan your work and budget. The moment you start neglecting recreation, stress starts going up.

Most importantly, start appreciating life for its merits. Find time to praise life, nature and all the things that fill you with happiness. If you like something, then take out time to look at it more attentively. If anything attracts you, then pursue it.

Living life consciously is the beginning of starting your journey towards leading a stress-free life. Remain mindful of the life around you.

The Role Of Habits In Reducing Stress And Mind Clutter

Clutter at the physical, emotional, or psychological level causes stress. It is one of the biggest reasons for stress.

The physical clutter is obvious. Any excess material that's of no use to you is clutter. Anything that may have been used a long time ago but hasn't been put to use for more than a year is clutter.

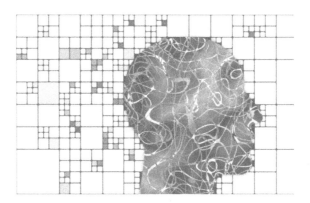

Clearing Physical Clutter is Easy

Clutter takes up space and energy. It uses up your productive energy and distracts you. Your focus can keep deviating if there is clutter around you. Clutter always reminds you that there is one job left to be sorted and you haven't done it. It has a great impact on your functioning and efficiency. You can sort physical clutter by simply removing the unnecessary items from your vision. You can make the system and workplace leaner and things would be better.

Strategy To Overcome

Think of Others Who are in Need:

Take time in your life to stop and give thought to others in the world that is in dire need of help. Many people in the world suffer terribly not knowing where or if they will have a meal each and every day. They have no proper homes, no clean drinking water many die each and every day from ailments that they didn't have to die from. If they only had food and clean drinking water to sustain them like you have. These are people that would gladly trade places with you who have a home, food and clean drinking water but yet you are still unhappy.

Sometimes it takes looking at what others do not have to realize how much you do have and how blessed you are to have the life you have. It may not be your perfect idea of a life but that is up to you to make choices that will improve the quality of your life. At least you have the freedom and options to make choices for yourself many do not have the freedoms you have.

Stop Feeling Sorry for Yourself:

Instead of going on a self-pity trip perhaps you should instead try and focus on more positive things. When you feel yourself going into a depressive state where you think you are so hard done to stop and take a moment to think of all the people in the 3rd world countries that are dying of starvation each and every day while you sit feeling sorry for yourself.

Take this time and use it in a positive way such as making a donation to a charity either financial or by giving your time. You will feel much better than you would just lie around your home buried deep in a self-pity trip. You must get up and dust yourself off and begin taking actions in your life that will lead you to that happier life you seek but just remember to think about those who are less fortunate while doing so.

How To Overcome

However, things are not as easy with mental clutter. Our mind is processing thoughts 30 times faster than the fastest supercomputer in the world. It handles more than 1016 processes in a second. Even when you are not thinking about it, your mind is continuously taking decisions.

For instance, take lunch one afternoon:

You are still in your cubical punching keys on your computer. But, as soon as your mind gets a fragrance of food, it starts thinking about it. The mind doesn't think in a restrained manner. It goes full throttle.

There are thoughts of things you want to eat at lunch, you would want but can't have. Would you be able to get a specific item in the lunch? Would it taste good? Would someone accompany you?

Most of the times, you are not even paying attention to it. Your active participation isn't even required. Your mind is capable of thinking all these in-between things. However, one thing that makes this a problem is that this thinking requires decision making. There are choices to be made.

Whenever there are choices to be made, your mind gets stuck. This activity requires your active participation. The mind wouldn't simply stop at giving you the choices but would question your decisions. This creates a dilemma and any kind of dilemma or hesitation will lead to mental clutter.

You are making thousands of such insignificant decisions in your day. Your mind keeps coming at the points where it requires a decision. It questions those decisions. It debates on the success or failure of those decisions. All this leads to the generation of mental clutter. Any kind of clutter will bombard your mind with excessive stimuli. Your mind would go on an overdrive. There will be unnecessary distraction and hesitation. There will be the physical, mental, and emotional stress of making such decisions. Your mind constantly keeps receiving messages that there is still work pending. It never comes to rest leading to fatigue. It creates anxiety and you may also feel the guilt or repentance of taking decisions. It inhibits your creativity, productivity, and problem-solving abilities. Countless activities of similar nature are running in the background.

All this leads to stress. If it continues for long, it converts into chronic stress and takes a toll on health. This is why people sitting at the position of great power start looking haggard and aged much earlier.

4. Secret To Dealing Your Stress And Anxiety For Good

Mental toughness is a state of being that pulls together a variety of skills, focus, and self-restraint to overcome adverse situations, setbacks, emotional upheaval, and stress/anxiety in order to accomplish a given goal. It is a type of sought-after "superpower" of sorts that most highly successful people have in abundance.

Stress, anxiety, worry, and defeatist attitudes prevent us from achieving our goals and reaching our highest potential. We freeze in our tracks and allow setbacks to define pivotal moments and recall past damage to justify future lack of progress. Mental toughness is about overcoming all the obstacles that we either place before ourselves or are placed before us. It involves learning to cope with life's challenges in order to succeed.

This gives you an edge in your professional life, personal life, love life, athletic activities, and basically anything else you can think of that requires more than a pulse. Put simply, mental toughness makes you more prepared for life.

Think about your ancestors who lived in a world without all of our modern comforts that not only make life pleasant but also safe. They didn't have cozy, cushy lives that protected them from any trace of harm. They couldn't avoid pain because it was a part of life. They displayed the epitome of mental toughness. Hunter/gatherers had to set out into the forest despite the dangers in order to live as well. If they allowed themselves to break down or get taken over by fear, they'd be dead.

Mental toughness is in your head, not your genes, and it certainly doesn't depend on your physical stature. Physical _toughness' doesn't have to accompany you physically—you can never have set foot in a gym and still be mentally tough. All you need is the —just do it ‖ m entalitythat Nike has so successfully marketed.

Can anyone develop mental toughness? Yes, it is possible if you take the time to find out what are the obstacles that cause you to fall off the track or not hit the mark. You can cultivate the same skill that the top echelon achievers naturally possess or so it appears.

How the Mind Works

The physical and electrical processes that take place inside the brain structure are relatively complex but are uniform in nature to every human. Differences and aberrations in the features of the brain can cause some differences in response, ability to fire neurons and give adequate reactions.

Energy use of the brain

A group of ambitious researchers at the University of Pennsylvania set out to determine some of the little-understood workings of the brain and its use of energy both at rest and during heavy use.

The first order of business was to come up with a baseline for determining how much the use of energy increased when doing any type of activity beyond rest. The measurement of oxygen used in the brain during activity was the simplest to measure. It turns out that the brain uses the maximum amount of energy in maintaining the firing of electrical energy throughout the brain. It never increased due to an increase in physical activity or thinking.

The good news with these results is that when you have the energy available to be in an awake state means that you have plenty of energy to tackle any thought-driven process or activity. Alertness and peak activity potentially happen at the midway point of a standard wake period, which varies by the individual.

Distraction potential

In the mid-1980s, a group of clinical psychologists at Michigan State University performed an informal study that involved 60 students conducting a variety of simple tests to determine the basis of brain activity. These students were given an essay to read with a brief questionnaire to answer after. One-half were told to ring a small bell during the time they were reading the essay. The other half were asked to ring the bell during the time period of answering the questions. Those that rang the bell during the reading portion were unable to answer as many questions correctly.

The takeaway on this portion of the informal study is that humans seem to become more distracted during a —thinking ‖ or preparation phase of a project. Those ringing the bell during the answering phase increased their speed in answering correctly. It points to an appreciable line to draw in the sand to eliminate the bad effects of distraction.

It is okay to talk to yourself!

Most people feel self-conscious when talking to themselves, especially if they notice that people are staring and wondering why they are doing it. You will feel good the following time someone tries to discredit you for talking to yourself. The human mind responds far more to verbal cues than quietly trying to remember something. It can be a quick way to move an item in your mind from the short-term to long-term memory storage.

Thoughts, Emotions, and Actions

The development of mental toughness will demand that your thoughts, emotions, and actions are reigned in and kept under tight control during the worst of situations and conditions. Exercise your skills to the point that jumping these hurdles can be as simple as breezing over physical hurdles for skilled athletes.

The basic way that the brain is designed and operates gives you leverage to develop a strong mental toughness for any situation. You can make a mental choice to develop the skills that will propel you towards success or remain quietly living in the background and feeling bitter that nothing about your life changes.

How natural brain activity benefits thoughts

Spending quality time thinking about solutions to problems or making plans to resolve issues seems to be draining and requires tons of extra energy. The truth is that you are using no more energy to think through things than what it takes to be in a waking state. Shake off the feelings of fatigue and understand that your mind is designed to do this effectively. Push past the barriers that are established over false thoughts that make you think that you do not have the energy to make changes in your life.

Distractions and emotions

Being in touch with your emotional side is critical to developing mental toughness. Knowing when emotions are trying to formulate and take over is the perfect time to introduce distraction techniques. You can easily learn how to pull yourself out of an emotional funk that keeps you bound up and unable to move forward. Mental weakness is rewarded through being pliable to raw emotion. It doesn't mean that you have to switch your emotions off completely. You can be a compassionate, feeling person that is not ruled by emotions.

The symbiotic relationship between the brain and body

The ability to formulate the right thoughts, distract to remove emotions, and actively give ourselves verbal instruction demonstrates the symbiotic relationship between our mind and body. Using the natural functions of the brain to your advantage to create a strong sense of mental toughness makes it a method that is both easy and takes a small amount of time to see positive results. You will be able to define your areas of weakness and strength right away. Shoring up your weaknesses will provide you with a stronger foundation for further mental toughening skills development.

Nature and Nurture

What are the factors that determine the way our brains are used? Are we more of a product of our environment or at the mercy of the natural tendencies inherent to all individuals? The short answer is that it is always a combination of both. Striking a balance of good qualities from nature and nurturing is the key to successfully reaching a state of ultimate usable mental toughness. You can retain a sensible approach to life that allows you to maneuver obstructions and obstacles easily.

Identifying negative natural tendencies

Every person has individualized ways of thinking about things and coming to conclusions. Often, these are influenced by natural tendencies or processes that are undergone without any preparation or thought. A few of these are:

- Not wanting to draw attention

- A desire for lack of any conflict

- A desire to not feel negative emotions

- Need for an easy solution

- Consistent problem avoidance

Knowing that you lean toward these natural tendencies can help alert you to seeing how this is affecting the way to think about and process situations. It can help motivate you to push away from a tendency not to think about a problem or look for the simplest solution. Mentally tough individuals are more likely to look for a solution that provides a concrete and fair outcome. You should never avoid thinking about a problem because it brings in negative feelings or causes you to deal with difficult emotions.

Identifying learned behaviors

Non-productive behaviors in our thinking and processing of events can also come from our nurturing and environment. A few examples of this are:

- Being raised in a household with indecisive parental figures

- Having people around that are highly-emotionally charged

- Not addressing situations or problems at all

- Leaving the solutions open-ended to try and please everyone

Being a people-pleaser and unwilling to confront emotional decisions can take you further away from a state of mental toughness than anything else. Tough situations sometimes call for tough decisions. You need to develop these skills if you have been raised in an environment that focuses on trying to make all parties happy. In the end, you will consistently feel like you sold out and are never satisfied with the progress made in life. Mental toughness can be achieved without feeling like you have been heartless, cruel, or discounted the feelings of others.

Turn Negative Thinking Into Positive Thinking

Rewiring your negative thoughts into positive thoughts is all about changing your thought processes. The shift can be intentional or coincidental.

The former way allows you to take control of the thinking process to move towards your goal of positive thoughts. Rewiring your attention to a more positive point can prompt you to be happier. For intentionality to be effective, one needs to be specific on turning their negative thoughts into positive ones.

Practically speaking, you can do this by connecting formerly negative experiences with positive expectations. An example is changing your thought process from considering a scenario that would cause you to be anxious to one of being an opportunity to improve. Adjusting responses to situations could turn situations into positive ones. The act can be a form of building a growth mindset. You may also choose to avoid thoughts that have negative consequences like depression. Such feelings can lead to negative neuroplasticity as they encourage the formation of detrimental mental connections. The result may be a worsening of the effects of negative thought patterns through the development of a negative feedback loop system.

Embracing a growth mindset can assist in developing a higher capacity to endure adverse events. Such a mindset can lead to an increase in perseverance. Adopting a relaxed viewpoint can further support the process of turning thoughts from negative to positive.

Learning cognitive skills can aid your process of rewiring your negative thoughts into positive ones. These skills will provide you with a framework for handling varying considerations that accompany or occur as issues arise.

A healthy lifestyle does play a role in rewiring your thoughts from negative to positive. Choose diets that support brain function.

STRATEGY 4

HOW TO RECOGNIZE NEGATIVE THOUGHTS

LEARN TO OVERCOME THEM

Overcoming Negative Thoughts That Control Your Life

We agree that negative thoughts are the thoughts that make you miserable and sad; the kind that causes you to dislike yourself and other people. Depending on the manner you choose to express them and the length of time you allow them to affect you, these negative thoughts will dampen the enthusiasm you have for life.

Negative thoughts will also keep you from behaving and thinking rationally, from seeing situations through a clear, unbiased lens. When this happens, you see things how your mind wishes to interpret them, and you remember only what your mind wants to remember. This is a flawed way of viewing and experiencing life because it keeps you from dealing with the reality, and the problem with this view of life is that it only prolongs your frustration, anger, and disappointment. In addition, the longer you hold on to false beliefs, the more entrenched the prevailing issue will get. On that account, failure to deal with your negative thoughts appropriately is harmful. Have you ever wondered why people possess different reactions all the time? Sometimes the results become so weird that other people become affected. In some situations, this can be even worse, while other times, it is just displaying positively. If you are not aware, then this is an emotion. It comes in different shapes and from different angles. That's, you can experience thoughts the whole of your life span.

Therefore, emotion may refer to a mental state related to your nervous system and always caused by chemical changes. That's, the sentiment is an amalgamation of various feelings, thoughts, and even behavioral responses. Also, thoughts can include some degrees of displeasure and pleasure. Therefore, you cannot define an emotion since it comprises many issues. In most cases, it talks much about our moods, disposition, and even personality. Again, thoughts involve motivation and temperament.

Many scientists, day in day out are working hard in their various fields to come up with the best definitions of thoughts. However, this effort renders futile. Even though research is increasing daily, no better description of emotion will define the word emotion. Our feelings range from happiness to sadness, frustrations to fear, depression to disappointment, and all these have either negative or positive impacts on our life. Thoughts are always complicated. They are biological and psychological, and because of that, our brains respond to them by releasing chemicals and hormones, which later send us into an arousal state of mind. Surprisingly, all thoughts result from this process. That's both negative and positive thoughts.

There are five primary emotions which control our daily life. We have anger, surprise, sadness, fear, and even disgust. Remember, there are other thoughts, which include frustrations, confidence, cruelty, apathy, boredom, and much more. Positive thoughts can increase our daily productions within the various companies we are. Again, they improve our wellbeing and instill in us that nourishment we dearly need in our life. These positive thoughts include happiness, joy, kindness, and confidence, among others. Always we strive to have the best but believe me; no one will ever experience total pleasure forever in their lives. As a result, they, at one point, will get frustrated, annoyed, and at some point, engulfed in a quagmire of anger. During this time, everything might come to a standstill. That's if it was a specific task being done, then its completion might be in jeopardy.

Recognizing Negative Thoughts

The first step to dealing with negative thoughts is to recognize and to decode them. To decode an emotion is to slow the emotion or thought process involved, as though you had hit the slow mode on a remote, so that you watch the process frame by frame, systematically, until you find meaning in what is happening.

When people realize that they are having negative reactions towards other people or a situation, they are often quick to take up measures to reverse their reaction.

The first step towards dealing with the negative situation is to identify the negative emotion that lies underneath. Identifying the actual feeling will provide you with incredible insight into why you act the way you do. Therefore, it will allow you to approach the same situation from a different perspective. The principle here is that for you to understand clearly, what you are dealing with, you must first identify the driving emotion.

Identify The Trigger Thought Or Event

Think back to what was crossing your mind when you started feeling as you do right now. It may take a minute to roll back the tape as far back as you can remember. What do you find therein that could have caused your negative thoughts? There was likely an event or something that happened to you, something you saw or interaction you had with someone that dampened your mood.

From there, now think about the mental response you gave to what happened. Could you have thought that the situation will never improve, you are not good enough, you will never succeed, you always take the blame, or that you have had enough? Whatever statement rushed into your mind, take note of it and write it down. Once you have done that, it's time to proceed to step two.

5. Decluttering Your Thoughts

If you had to answer what your most scarce resource is, what would the answer be? Would time be your answer? Time certainly feels like it's never enough, yet time itself is constant and does not change. You don't have more or less of it on any given day. 24-hours are all we have and that is it. Nothing more, nothing less. Living in the information age we do today, it's not time that's the scarcest resource, it's our attention span. Ever since the internet came about, the amount of information that we receive has increased dramatically. The problem is, the amount of information we can process at any given time remains the same. As a result, we're faced with information overload, a problem that has been growing ever since the internet starting booming. The bigger the internet becomes and the more reliant we are on it, the more overloaded our brains become.

Information is addictive and we can't quite seem to stay away from it even when we're already taking on more than we can handle. Just look at the number of hours we spend scrolling aimlessly through social media taking in the updates, the status shares, the likes, the pictures, the videos. It's a lot to process for a brain that doesn't do well under multitasking pressure. Processing and absorbing information is becoming increasingly more difficult, evident in today's corporate environments in particular. One study by the Pew Research Center discovered that in an already oversaturated world, 20% of the American respondents surveyed say they overloaded by the amount of information they receive. Yet, 77% of those respondents stated that they liked having a lot of information easily available, while 67% say having a lot of information helps to simplify their lives. It turns out Americans are pretty comfortable and confident in their ability to cope with the everyday flow of information they receive.

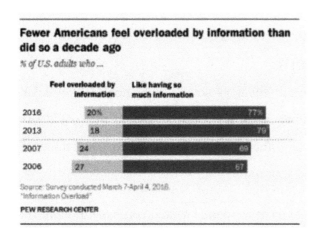

Image Source: Pew Research Center

Being able to cope, though, does not mean that this is good for the brain. Clutter exists for a reason, and if we continue to ignore the subtle signs of its presence (anxiety, stress, overthinking, negativity, depression) it's not going to stop until you put a stop to it. Not everyone processes information in the same way and if you're one of those that often feel stressed by how much you have to take it, it's an indicator that you're taking on more than you can handle and it's time to slow down and declutter.

Is Information Overload Serious?

Information overload is what happens to the brain when it starts taking in more information can it can keep up with and process. In 2010, Google decided to count what they believed to be every available book in the world. The number they arrived at were a staggering 129,864,880 number of books. That was in 2010. A decade later, it's more than likely that number has tripled today. We're receiving more information in a single day than let's say, someone several decades ago in the 1600s, 1700 or 1800s did in one lifetime.

Google's current estimates of existing web pages are in the trillions. Trillions. Blogging statistics reveal that approximately 70 million new content on average is being published on WordPress in a month. Is it any wonder then that information overload has become a prevalent problem?

Having a lot of information published online is not a problem. The fact that people keep adding information online is not a problem. The problem is we become so overwhelmed by everything that we're reading, watching, listening and processing that it starts getting increasingly more difficult to single out quality information from the crowd. The information that adds value to your life and benefits you. Half-baked articles and posts are a dime a dozen online, and most of the time when something doesn't hold our interest long enough, we skip over it or don't bother reading it at all. It is only when something catches your eye that you want to stop and consume it out of curiosity. More than that, you feel like you have to consume it. That's the problem.

No matter what the topic of interest may be, there are hundreds of other websites or blogs out there publishing the same thing. That's excluding the social media content, forums and other platforms that might be talking about the topic you're keen on too. The amount of information on one single subject of interest can be epic, that's the problem. When you feel like you want to consume it all and get to know everything that you can about the subject, but you don't have enough time to do it, you become overworked. Overloaded. Overwhelmed by all the clutter that is gathering in your brain because you can't process it quickly enough.

Information overload is not just a problem. It's a plague and given how reliant our lives have become on it, there is no cure. The only possible cure to curb the impact that it has on us is through self-control and a few good measures to declutter your thoughts whenever you feel there's too much information coming in at once.

Why Do We Experience Information Overload?

For one thing, we have widespread access to the internet to thank for the significant increase in the amount of accessible information. With everything being a quick Google search away, it's hard not to get swept up in the sea of information as soon as you log in to any device. Since information can be easily duplicated for free, anyone with access to the internet the right skills can disseminate information online, adding even more information. We need to remember that all of this online information is only a small part of the information we're absorbing on a daily basis. The sights, smells, sound, tastes, the emotions we feel, the words we read, the body language signals we're picking up from others, even the conversations we have. All of this is still information that is being processed and picked up by the brain.

Information overload is not doing your brain or your memory any favors. Overload, as we have learned, leads to mental blocks and sometimes a complete shutdown altogether. Especially when the brain is faced with more complex information that requires more processing time. When the brain is under pressure, sometimes it freezes and panics, stopping dead in its tracks. When that happens, we lose our ability to think clearly, the mind often goes —blank ‖ (som eth ing you w ou ld have no doub t experienced on m ore than one occasion) and that's when it starts to feel like it's all too much. Obviously, information overload is a lot more serious than we thought.

Other factors that could lead to this undesirable overload include:

- Too Many Choices - Choices are great, but too much of a good thing, as it turns out, can backfire. With so many options and no idea which one to choose, it can feel like you're being pulled in a million different directions, making it even harder to concentrate and pay attention.

- Emails - An overlooked contributor to the clutter we feel brought on by information, the emails that keep flooding our inbox every day are a massive contributor to the mental clutter we feel. It doesn't help matters that probably more than half the email content you receive is either spam or not important enough to invest any time in. Phil Chambers, author of Brilliant Speed Reading indicated that research estimated approximately 247 billion emails get sent on average worldwide per day, 81% of which is spam. That is a considerable amount of information that gets channeled through email.

- Social Media - Let's face it. We've got more social media platforms than we need. Facebook, Instagram, Twitter, Snap Chat, Pinterest and more take up far too much of our time as we spend scrolling and searching without any real purpose or intention. You tell yourself you're only going to check these social media apps for a couple of minutes, but the next thing you know half an hour has gone by and you've fallen behind on a task you should have started. Not to mention the pointless clutter you've now filled your mind with. Very rarely does social media provide any useful content.

- News - Today's media dissemination is relentless. Yet, we can't help ourselves. The thirst for knowing what's going on is a pull that is too hard to resist. With attention spans becoming shorter by the day, the constant need for the —new ‖ and —latest ‖ information, news channels are only feeding into this need with their short news cycle and almost 24/7 content publication.

Information Overload Is Never Good

We spend so much time worrying, overthinking, and overanalyzing that we don't have time to step back and assess the way we're impacted by information overload and the way it aggravates our worries. We react at what life happens to throw our way instead of evaluating what's best for us. Several years ago, we didn't have the time-saving apps and technology to make it a little easier to navigate everyday life, yet people back then were probably less stressed than we are today. The one advantage they did have back then was not being faced with a deluge of options and a constant flow of information nearly every minute of every day.

Information overload is a problem when it stops you from taking action. The stream of information that comes pouring in is endless, and you'll never be able to keep up fast enough to take it all in and the stress that is gained indirectly from trying to keep up with everything is only going to wear you down. Even wore, when you're overloaded, the tendency to procrastinate is higher than ever when it's hard to think clearly or stay focused on what you need to do. Procrastination is one path that leads directly to laziness. Some other negative side effects you're like to experience when your brain is overworked and so cluttered it can't think straight include:

- Diminishing Motivation - Motivation is the push that gets us through the activities we ordinarily would not want to do. When there is a lack of motivation or inspiration to do anything that opens the door for procrastination to start creeping in slowly. As your motivation starts to dwindle, the tendency to waste even more precious time aimless scrolling through the information that doesn't benefit you (like the content you get on social media) increases.

- You Remain Trapped in a Negative Mindset- An overloaded brain will find it hard to escape the cycle of negativity. That's because being negative is always the easier option, being positive requires a lot more effort put into it. The danger with a lot of the information we're consuming is that there is more negative content out there, making it easy for our brains to latch on to it quickly. Negative content will always be the first thing that grabs your attention because the brain is hardwired toward the negativity bias, meaning that it seeks out negative information first before anything else.

6. Challenge Your Thoughts Before Things Blow Out Of Proportion

It is easy for someone to get carried away into negative chains of thought. Sometimes you tend to conclude things even before they actually even happen. For example, some people think that calling in sick will get them fired.

So they end up overthinking things and maybe go to work even though they were unfit to work in the first place. Some people even go to great lengths that they will become homeless if they don't meet their certain deadline.

One of the things that you can do in this situation is to challenge your thoughts. Recognize that you are exaggerating the negative.

How Healthy Thoughts Can Help

There are several benefits of healthy thinking that have been identified by experts:

- They help to reduce worry and also fear

- They may help people with anxiety (though this may not always be enough)

- After practicing it for some time, healthy thinking can come naturally to people

- CBT has been found to help improve healthy thoughts

Here are several ideas how challenging your thoughts and healthy thinking can help you cope with anxiety and stress and thus reduce overthinking.

Take Time To Notice And Stop Your Thoughts

The first step is to identify them times when you're having negative self-talk. Some self-talk is positive and affirming. However, if you overthink things then notice that there will be more times when your self-talk or internal monologue tends to be negative.

When you notice that things are swaying towards the negative—then you must stop.

Here are some hallmarks of negative self-talk that you should pay attention to:

• Highlighting the negative

Some people call this as positive filtering. For instance, when asked to speak in public you may begin to think that people are looking for ways you will blunder your way during your talk.

However, with a little bit of reality check you will notice that no one is actually paying attention to your performance other than yourself. They care more about the information you presented rather than the way you presented it.

TIP : Always perform a reality check when negative thoughts filter through.

• Mental filter

This is when you filter out all the good things about yourself and only highlight the negative things. It's like saying, I never did anything good in my life, but you just helped your neighbor get their trash out.

• Overgeneralizing

Be wary of words like —always ‖ and —never ‖ and other over generalized terms. They sometimes pop up with negative thoughts. For instance, when you tell yourself that you will —never amount to anything ‖ you should take a minute to challenge that thought.

Do another reality check; are you really —never ‖ going to amount to anything? What success have you achieved lately? The smallest success already proves that generalized assessment as false.

In fact, chances are, your overgeneralizations are just exaggerations.

• Disqualifying the positive

This is when you disqualify even the good things that you have done. For instance, you weren't late for work, but you then tell yourself that you were only two seconds away from being late again, which undermines your performance as an employee. You did something good but your thoughts disqualify and overshadow it with something negative.

• All or nothing thinking

Another thing to watch out for is all or nothing thinking. It's like —if I don't' ace this interview, I will never be successful. ‖ Take the time to challenge that assessment. Ask yourself; is this the last job interview you will ever have?

Of course not—you will still find other opportunities and some may even be better than this one they are offering. Beware of the all or nothing thinking; a lot of times it leans towards the negative.

• Emotional reasoning

This is when your emotions become your basis for the truth. For example, I feel sad today, maybe this is going to turn out to be a bad day for me.

• Jumping to conclusions

This is when you extrapolate small negative experiences and making up something bigger out of them. For instance, you made a bad joke in front of your boss. You immediately think that your boss sees you as the next guy to get fired because he didn't like your joke.

• Personalization

This is when you make negative experiences caused by your person or personal even if it is obvious that they were not. For example, you think that the party was a disappointment because I wasn't entertaining enough.

• Catastrophic thinking

This is when you always assume that the worst possible scenario is going to happen. So, the world is facing a global pandemic. You think that the world is going to end? Before you run off to a bunker and seal your stash of goods that will last you in the next 3 years or so, challenge that thought.

Ask yourself: is this the first global pandemic that human beings have faced? The answer is that it isn't. And the fact is that we are getting better at addressing such problems. One day we will get even better and the more will our societies and governments be prepared to face such a crisis.

• Magnification/minimization

This is when you exaggerate your own mistakes and then you minimize your own achievements. For instance, you tell yourself, yes I won that contract, but then you highlight the fact that you had to reduce the price of your quotation thus your company wasn't able to maximize profits which is something that your boss might frown upon and maybe this incident will be grounds for delaying your promotion.

Learning To Choose Your Thoughts

Now that you have learned to identify which thoughts you need to stop and challenge, the next step is to learn how to replace those thoughts. Assess the situation and assess your thoughts.

Challenge them and do a reality check. Sometimes, you may need to call for help to make that reality check for you. It can be a friend, a mentor, your spouse, your kin, or even a parent. Sometimes a therapist may be a good resource person to give you that much needed reality check.

After identifying your triggers and negative thought patterns, it is time to record them and create alternatives to them. One tool that will help you do just that is something called a thought journal or a though diary.

How A Thought Journal Can Help

A thought journal will help you keep a record of your thought patterns. When you keep a record of your thoughts the more aware you are of the way you think, and the better you will be at coping against such thoughts.

The more you realize how you think things through the better you are at stopping yourself from thinking negatively, the better you are at challenging your negative thoughts, and you can constructively compose better and alternative thoughts.

A thought journal also makes you aware of your negative self-talk. Any negative thoughts that you may be holding should be written down as soon as they come to you. You can't always keep track of your thoughts, which is why a notepad will be a great tool so you can identify thinking patterns.

It will take some practice before you make this a habit, but the important thing is that you get it started ASAP. Note that some of your negative thoughts may hold a kernel of truth.

If that is the case then you should acknowledge that truth no matter how small it is. However, you should also correct the other false assumptions that you have made with it. Remember that the little truth is all there is, the rest of the thought is just blowing things out of proportion.

Now, when you make your journal entries, you should create three sections:

1. The negative thought – this is where you just write down the raw negative thoughts that come to your mind. Keep the space below that thought and the page right after that one blank. Every subsequent negative thought you have should be written in the next sheet.

2. Classification – Right after the record of your negative thought, a few lines underneath it actually, you should write down a classification of that negative thought. It can be any of the items that were mentioned above like overgeneralizing, focusing too much on the negative, catastrophic thinking, etc. it doesn't have to be a technical classification.

It's just a way for you to account for the types of thoughts that you're having. That way you'll understand what thought patterns you normally have. Some people tend to overgeneralize more while others tend to highlight the negative more than anything.

3. Accurate and positive alternative thought – this is where you write down the reality check that you will be making that will help you challenge your negative thoughts. This is your alternative and more factual assessment of the situation. Call it the rational side of things that are based on actual facts.

So, for instance, going back to the previous example earlier, let's say you were asked by your boss to give a short message for the company's 10th year anniversary. Your thoughts went crazy and you begin to feel nervous about the message that you're expected to give.

Start recording those thoughts in your journal. Start with ―I get nervous about this assignment because… ‖

Let the intro be short and direct to the point. Add every detail that comes to your mind about the train of negative thoughts that come to you. Yes, sometimes negatives come in bunches.

So let's say, for example, you have written the following entry:

―I am so nervous about this speaking assignment from my boss that I think that my coworkers are going to laugh at me. I hate being the laughing stock in this company and I don't want to disappoint my boss.

I know I am bad at public speaking. I think I'm such a big introvert. I wasn't meant for this. I haven't given speeches my entire life. ‖

After that long tirade of thoughts, you can draw a horizontal line across the page. Under the page you will then write the classification of that train of negative thoughts.

For this example we can say that this negative is all about highlighting the negative and overgeneralizing. Well, for one thing, the thoughts highlight your inexperience at giving talks but it also generalizes things not considering the possibility that you may have a knack for entertaining the crowd with your wits.

Your boss chose you for a reason, right? Then maybe there is something in you that your boss saw. A hidden capability that you weren't able to spot in yourself. If you can think of other categories that your negative thought fits into then add it there as well.

Finally, the last part of your thought journal is the positive feedback or reality check. Again, we have already done that somewhat. For instance, your boss chose you for a reason. He had confidence in you and maybe he saw your potential.

The Emotion Or Reaction You Gave

What feeling went with the thought or reaction you gave? Identify the thoughts you are having. Is it anger, frustration, fear, loneliness, or pain? From the list of thoughts, you might identify one or two of those. Write those down, and you can proceed to the third step.

Identify The Physical Manifestation Of Your Emotion

What are you feeling in your body, or how is your body reacting to your thoughts? Are your fists clenched? Does your face feel hot? Do you have stiffness in your neck or a headache? Is there pain in your stomach? The physical manifestation varies from one person to the other, and there are no wrong answers here. Only take your time to identify how your body may have changed. Besides, you are learning a new skill, and it requires patience and full attention. Once you have identified the said sensation, put it down on paper also.

By now, you have a _chain' of events listing the negative thought, the emotion you felt, and the reaction or sensation that followed. Let's see an example:

—I am the only one who seems to care ‖ --- Loneliness, Frustration, anxiety --- Headache, Hot Face

Walk Away From Any Negative Thought Patterns

Patterns are typically repetitive, which means that negative thought patterns allow negative, unhelpful thoughts to repeat themselves. As you would expect, this process yields negative, unpleasant, and unwanted thoughts like depression, fear, anxiety, shame, unworthiness, and stress. As such, the key to avoiding negative thoughts is to cut out the negative thought patterns in the first place.

Become Aware

From your experiences, you must have noticed that your negative thoughts flow from two distinct directions: dwelling on issues of the past and worrying about what is to be in the future. When you dwell on the past, you mostly ruminate over mistakes, guilt, problems, and issues in the past that did not go as you had hoped they would. On the other hand, people worry about the future because they are afraid of what might or might not happen in the future, for themselves and others.

Practice Mindfulness Daily

As we grow and become more taken by our problems, desires, hopes, goals, and dreams, we forget the deep, inborn peace and pure unconditioned inborn awareness that is entrenched deeply in all of us. In this state, it is easy to be so drawn into your negative thoughts that you lose your sense of self.

In reality, your mind is like an ocean on which surface waves will cause great tumult on the surface, yet the depths remain unaffected and peaceful. Inside you perfect stillness, just beneath your thoughts, habits, and conditioning, tend to be tumultuous. Beneath all that is an undeniable quiet that serves as a calm refuge, and it is always available for you.

Distinguishing Helpful From Unhelpful Thoughts

Getting rid of some negative thoughts can be quite difficult, resisting both the identification and the mindfulness approach. If you are in a situation like this, and you discover that some thoughts are _sticky,' there remains an approach you can take to untangle yourself from your thoughts. This approach involves asking yourself some helpful questions to challenge unhelpful thoughts and redirect your focus.

Strategies To Overcome

Remember to Tell Your Loved Ones You Love Them:

A good habit to get into that will not only make your loved ones feel better in hearing it but it will also boost your mood is tell them you love them. Don't take your loved ones for granted and just presume that they know that you love them, so you don't bother telling them. It is always nice to hear and reassuring when you hear a person say that they love you out loud. It helps to seal the bond with your loved ones keeping the relationships healthy by communicating clearly to others.

Don't cut yourself off from friends and family reach out to them for their support and you will get it. But you must be willing to let them know what is going on with you and try and talk about your feelings. Family counseling can be a good way to get some good advice on how to improve your relationships with loved ones. Try and be positive and give compliments to your loved ones not negative hurtful comments that can leave deep scars on a person's heart. If you have nothing good to say, then don't say anything. If you think positive thoughts, you should share them with others.

Giving Thanks Daily:

There is so much in life that you should be thankful for each and every day; try and give thanks on some level each and every day. Point out things that others do for you to make your life better each and every day and make sure you acknowledge these things and give thanks to those that give them to you. If you are a religious person remember to give thanks to your higher power for giving you the life you live today. But just remember the power to improve your life lies in your hands; you must be the one to take the steps towards the healthier happier life no one can take these steps for you. Good luck in your journey to less worrying and more enjoying life to the fullest!

How To Overcome

Every time try as much as possible to keep in touch with every detail of your thoughts, especially the negative ones. By doing this, you create that self-awareness of yourself, thus, increasing your personal touch within you. In most cases, even in various companies and other organizations, the most critical trait of a leader will always be self-awareness. That's the ability to be able to monitor the thoughts and reactions of everyone. Mastering the skills of self-awareness sometimes proves to be problematically sophisticated or difficult tasks. However, when you can find good ways to help you learn, then this will be of great help.

Remember, being an effective leader needs much of self-awareness than anything else. However, it is good to note that most of you will avoid self-reflection, which can emulate you in knowing your self-awareness. You will end up getting feedback about your personality from various people. Nevertheless, in most cases, this will be full of honesty and flattery since no one would wish to tell you the real truth about yourself if, at all, it embraces some harmful elements. Along the process, you will not get a good perspective view of your self-awareness from outside people. Therefore, because of these, you might harbor a low level of self-awareness without your knowledge.

As a result of these, it is better to look at the various ways you can use to increase your self-awareness. In the end, you will realize that you are developing your self-awareness, and these will help you tremendously in dealing with your negative thoughts.

STRATEGY 5

OVERCOMING THE ADDICTIVE RELATIONSHIP

What Are Addictive Relationships

Perhaps you have taken an appraisal of the relationship, you know what a healthy relationship is, and you have categorized the relationships in your life. Still, some relationships are quite difficult to quantify. If you experience feelings such as emptiness, sadness, incompleteness, and despair in any of your relationships, it is safe to say that the relationship is an unhealthy or addictive.

Before speaking about it, we must first determine what an addictive relationship is. When one partner shows obsessive attention to the other, with little regard or attention for themselves, that relationship can be termed an addiction. These sorts of relationships are characterized by one individual's desire to connect and remain connected to their partner. This type of obsession manifests itself by making the individual in question understand that while the relationship might be unhealthy for them, they, for some reason, are unable to leave.

Individuals that are involved in addictive relationships tend to daydream and obsessively consider their partner. This overwhelming desire to think of their partner could cause them to have unrealistic hopes in their partner. This translates to giving an undue amount of their time and energy towards them. Typically, in a relationship, both partners create boundaries early on that help demarcate what is healthy and what isn't. These boundaries tend to erode in an addictive relationship. This is expressed by an individual willingly choosing to do anything or give anything up to ensure the survival of that relationship. It isn't just boundaries that become eroded in this situation; confidence can also be negatively influenced. An addictive relationship has the power to stop those in it from trying to be better in their personal life or to attain the highest positions in their professional lives.

It is easy for an outsider to ask those participating in an unhealthy relationship to leave logically. However, while these types of relationships can be painful, logic and rationality tend to be of no use when those in the relationship discover that they are unable to leave. Finding out that the relationship you are in is a harmfully addictive and unhealthy one is never the tricky part. The difficult part is trying to reconcile the need to leave for your self-preservation with the stronger, intense piece of you that either feels helpless on the topic of leaving or chooses not to do anything about it.

The Psychology Behind Addictive Relationships

One thing to be clear about when discussing harmfully addictive relationships is that the individuals involved do not set out with the intent to become addicted to love. They seek relationships with the very best of intentions. Everybody wants to be in a relationship that is healthy and happy. That being said, there is always an underlying battle with intimacy under that good intention. Addiction, regardless of it being of sex or love, typically stems from a feeling of insecurity. This manifests as an ulterior motive. There are numerous reasons for their insecurity, with the major one is that the individual's family life could be one full of dysfunction. This dysfunction then causes individuals to search for a love object to put paid to any matters of childhood that were unfinished. While a dysfunctional childhood relationship can be blamed, it isn't always the relationship that individual had with their parents that requires repeating. At times, the unresolved relationship in question could be one with any family member. This is a cycle that is bound to continually happen in whatever relationship that individual enters unless they can resolve this by mourning their childhood losses and start acknowledging their feelings. When this is done, that individual becomes able to select relationships that are much more positive.

For individuals with such tendencies who are looking to steer clear from addictive relationships, it is best to take the time out to know your prospective partner. This is an essential step to take before becoming romantically or sexually involved with one another. It has been proven that by allowing yourself to fall in love right after meeting someone. Having blurry vision increases the likelihood of you attaching yourself to any individual that exhibits an unhealthy, yet familiar pattern.

It is necessary for individuals that are addicted to love to become reacquainted with reality. A hallmark sign of potential addiction is an individual having intense fantasies in which their love interest can fulfill their dreams and make them happy. Another behavior these sorts of individuals are prone to is the desire to project their feelings onto individuals they aren't too well acquainted with. The result of these emotions is a chemical high, which makes them feel good. While they feel good, these desires are not based in reality, nor are they factual because they do not know the object of their fanciful affection. This type of information is only gained by spending time with that person and experiencing them. The process by which addictive relationships function is by creating fanciful highs during the process of pairing. Whereas a healthy relationship grows and starts to become settled as time goes on, an addictive one never achieves equilibrium. An addictive relationship is sudden love, hopes, and fantasies, with no room for slow growth, causing it to burn out faster. Individuals in these types of relationships discover that they struggle to settle any natural differences that might occur when two people come together. In a healthy relationship, these difficulties are all part and parcel of getting to know one another. As stated earlier, a relationship cannot succeed unless there is honesty in it; an addictive relationship bucks the trend as it is a relationship without honesty. The truth becomes so much a foreign concept in a relationship like this that any underlying dynamics are either ignored or faked. This can translate to the relationship lacking real intimacy.

Real intimacy can be defined as the capability of and having the environment to freely speak on any matter that is risky or causes vulnerability. In its true essence, true intimacy eschews deflecting or apportioning blame as methods to evade being responsible.

It can be said that individuals who become addicted to relations have experienced childhood trauma. Trauma, in this sense, is the fact that they discovered frequently enough that it was better to keep one's real identity, thoughts and beliefs safe away when interacting with others. This decision was derived as a coping mechanism to ensure that their true essence was preserved, and they were unable to suffer disappointment. This caused them to have detached feelings. Coping mechanisms as such bring in toxic dynamics when perpetuated in adult relationships.

The Dangers Associated With Harmfully Addictive Relationships

Before fixing any issue, you are involved in; you must first recognize and acknowledge the dangers associated with them. It is no different from an addictive relationship. You have to be able to understand what risks an addictive relationship poses to you. You should also recognize any addictive traits you might have that cause you to become intertwined with or attracted to addictive relationships. As with a healthy relationship, the feelings associated with addictive relationships might appear to be genuine fondness or deep attachment. This type of feeling, however, is prone to creating numerous adverse effects like alcoholism or drug addiction.

A harmfully addictive relationship is unbalanced one. This is manifested in one individual being wholly dependent on their partner. What this means is that any thoughts, decisions, or plans they make, have to be run by their partner. This does not happen because their partner requested it; instead, it happens since they believe that it is essential for the wellbeing of the relationship if their partner is kept abreast of every decision they make. This process of overdependence causes the individual in question not only to lose their identity, but it could also cost them their future, as their decision making becomes severely hampered. It is one thing to have and be in an unhealthy relationship; it is also another to have that relationship transform into controlling and overbearing. This transformation happens when the non-obsessive partner discovers the power given to them by the other individual. This loss of balance can significantly strain the relationship and also have the same effect on the obsessive individual without power.

A major point here is that addictions in a relationship are not the source of love. While it can mimic it, it isn't love. It is merely an addiction. A healthy relationship involves two individuals that are happy with each other, their personalities, their dreams and aspirations, and their entire beings. An addiction sullies that and causes an individual to not fall in love with who their partner is, but rather the idea and feeling of being connected to an ambiguous person. It is within this state that judgments begin to go awry, causing them to stay clear of logic and remain in a relationship or situation that ultimately is not for them. The result of a harmfully addictive relationship, regardless of its participants, is sadness and hurt.

How To Overcome

It does not matter if you already are in an addictive relationship, or you are concerned about slipping into one down the line; there are a couple of steps that you can use to ensure that harmful love addiction does not form. The following steps should be followed to avoid any opportunity of marital codependency forming:

You have to understand and value yourself. You should not let anyone make you dependent on them

You should discover what it is that makes you happy when you are in a relationship and work to get that

If you just left an addictive relationship, it is vital to allow some time to pass before inviting anyone else in so you can heal

You must acknowledge and work on any struggles from your past that negatively influence you currently

Recognize what an addictive relationship is at the initial stages and look to get help when formulating healthy boundaries

Discover ways to be apart while still being in a relationship. This could be with differing friend groups or varying activities

Develop a system of support which can be relied on. This support system should be separate from your partner.

STRATEGY 6

BUILD SELF-ESTEEM

What Is Self-Esteem?

Self-esteem is most commonly defined as how a person feels about themselves as a whole. There is often an emotional connection to a person's self-esteem that is not shared with confidence levels.

This trait is one that covers how an individual may feel about:

Their current life status

- Their current job status

- Their relationship status

- Their main hopes and how they are working toward them

- The people around them like friends and family

- Their physical strengths and where they want to work more

These are just some of the individual factors and variables that can shape a person's view of themselves and their self-esteem. If everyone in the world made a list of the points and traits they think about when they think about their view of themselves, you would most likely see many repeated important factors. However, another certainty that many experts and professionals who study the effects of self-esteem on people are that there will also be as many differences as there are similarities. The reason for this is that everyone has different values or expectations for themselves based on an additional variety of factors such as:

The environment they were raised in

- The family values instilled in them throughout childhood

- Their personal beliefs and values that have developed throughout their individual life experiences

- The expectations they set and the standards they hold themselves and those around them

These are just some of those additional factors that can help to shape an individual. The more in-depth someone looks into their thoughts, feelings, ideas, hopes, and dreams, the more they will know about themselves, and the higher their self-esteem will grow to be.

It Comes From: A person's self-esteem is most commonly shaped by their emotional experiences and encounters. The mistakes, triumphs, accidents, and successes throughout life all carry their own emotional and psychological influences with them. It's these influences that are most powerful when it comes to shaping how a person views themselves and their current lifestyle or life situation. The more positive influences and experiences a person can collect, the better their self-esteem will be. The more emotionally in control they will find themselves when stressful situations arise.

What Is Confidence (Or Self-Confidence)?

Confidence (particularly when described as self-confidence) refers to faith a person has in their knowledge, experience, skills, and abilities. Depending on how much belief someone has in the things they know, the things they say, and the things they do during their personal or professional interactions, the higher a person's confidence levels will be.

Where It Comes From?:

A person's confidence comes from their opinion of and trusts in their strengths and abilities. This trust and faith most often are the result of positive experiences such as promotions at work or awards at school. The more experience they have and proof they have been able to collect that they know what they are doing or what they are talking about, then the higher their self-confidence will be, and the more that will start to affect other areas of their life positively.

Many people have a high level of self-esteem. Still, they find that they lack confidence, especially in certain situations like when they are asked to do something without time to prepare or when they want to ask a question, but are concerned with how others will react to it. Hence, they decide just to keep their hand down. Alternately, people may have high levels of self-confidence and belief in their abilities, but also have poor levels of self-esteem from having their heart broken in a failed relationship or from trust issues that developed after being double-crossed by a friend or a co-worker.

Why Are These Traits So Important For Men & Women To Embrace, Develop & Strengthen?

As different as they can be, there are also plenty of situations and experiences caused by interconnected levels of self-esteem and confidence. The more understanding, experienced, and control a person has over their self-esteem and confidence levels, the better off they will be in all opportunities they attempt or goals they strive for throughout their life.

Strengthening these traits not only helps with improving a person's overall mental, psychological, and emotional health, but it also comes with a variety of other benefits that can help improve someone's health and wellness in a wide range of styles.

The Many Benefits Of Building Self-Esteem & Confidence

Even for those who are happy with their control over their customary overthinking and procrastination, there are an endless number of reasons to keep focused on and motivated to work on for anyone and everyone building self-esteem and confidence levels. Here is a look at some of the most popular and widely reported benefits people have experienced in their quests for higher self-esteem and confidence!

Those with higher self-esteem and personal confidence are less likely to be people pleasers or develop people-pleasing habits than those with lower opinions of themselves or their abilities

- They also tend to have better performance ratings and higher success rates in leadership roles

- Not only are they more personable with customers or other audiences, but they are also more empathetic with employers or co-workers and better able to boost morale during times of high demand or increased stress levels

- They are also more likely to have higher success rates with setting and reaching personal and professional goals because they are more self-aware of their mental, psychological, emotional changes and how it affects their daily performance

- Those with higher self-esteem and confidence levels report more personal and professional satisfaction throughout their lives

- They are more likely to take up opportunities when offered

- They also tend to be bolder and more dominant in their professional teams and social circles as they are more likely to openly share their opinions and start conversations with even those they do not know with more confidence than those who question themselves and hesitate around others

These are just a handful of the benefits that study and research subjects of all ages and lifestyles have reported when tracked over time and throughout their improvement journey! Each person will find a whole new array of benefits and progress markers that are specialized and more tailored to their individual needs based on the techniques they choose to put into practice, how dedicated they can remain to their self-improvement plan and of course, what specific issues and concerns that are working to improve or eliminate.

How To Get Started With Building Self-Esteem & Confidence Levels

Like with developing new positive habits to replace the damaging negative ones, the first step to getting started revolves around a person's self-awareness of their thoughts and emotions. The first thing anyone should do when trying to build their self-confidence and self-esteem is to take a look at their points of strength and points of concern. The following is an example of a self-awareness exercise that many people have reported progress during their quests for higher self-esteem.

A Self-Awareness Exercise: Get To Know Yourself & Your Restrictions

This self-awareness exercise is one of the most basic, one of the most widely used and one of the most effective, proven techniques for anyone trying to get a better idea of their highs and points where they may want to improve make the most of their potential.

Set aside a time where you can clear your mind and focus on the concerns at hand

- Make sure to deal with any potential distractions such as silencing your cell phone and turning off your television, perhaps even closing the door to the room you are going to be contemplating in so that you are not interrupted by anyone else in the building

- Layout a clean piece of paper and get the kind of pens that you when working on organizational thinking

- For some, they may just use a basic blue or black pen for anything they need to write, but when it comes to organization, some people prefer multiple colors or types of tips to choose from to separate different thoughts, ideas or options into color-coded or differently shaped areas

- Make a list of your strengths

- This can be emotional strengths like being able to remain calm in high-stress situations or always responding to friends and family the same day they message you

- This can be professional strengths like mastering a certain skill or getting recognition for something you accomplished in your department

- This can be personal strengths like organization and discipline, anything that you take pride in and use regularly

- Now flip the paper over or draw a line to separate your lists and make a list of your weaker points or skills that you want to develop and master

- Again, these points can be emotional like a tendency to breakdown when challenges arise in your personal or professional life

- They can be professional points of concern like wanting to be better at communicating with customers or being bolder when it comes to discussing a promotion with your employer

- They can also be personal, like a bad habit snapping at people who speak to you early in the morning or late in the day

- You do not have to make lists!

- Some people find that this exercise works better when they form connecting circles of related thoughts or pie charts of strengths, weaknesses and action plans

- The point is not to force your mind to start thinking in lists, but rather to find a way to organize your thoughts related to personal strengths, weaknesses, and goals for self-improvement.

Why This Exercise Works?:

This exercise has proven so effective for a variety of different personality types and characters because it can be tailored to work for any individual's particular way of thinking. Unlike most of the exercises and methods for overcoming negative psychological habits, this exercise does not require the person involved to change their mind or their thought processes but rather can be altered and specialized in working best for their particular way of organizing their thoughts.

Strategies To Overcome Lack Of Self-Esteem

Affirmations and Visualization

Affirmations and visualization are exercises in changing your mindset. If you're not happy with the mindset you have now, then clearly something needs to change. Besides working on developing the Growth Mindset, other approaches that are going to prove useful to you in this process are affirmations and visualization.

How Affirmations Work

Affirmations are essentially a set of positive, empowering statements. You repeat these statements to yourself often enough until they eventually influence your subconscious mind. The idea is to keep repeating these affirmations until you adopt this new set of beliefs. If you want to be happier, then your affirmation statement might sound like this: I am positive, and I am happy every day. French psychologist Émile Coué had a wonderful positive affirmation that is ideal for anyone wanting to achieve overall life improvements in general. His affirmation was this: —Every day in every way, I am getting better and better. ‖ Beautiful, simplistic, and effective. Exactly the kind of affirmation you need to change the way you think.

For affirmations to be effective, you need to believe in them. Really believe in them and not spout them off because it's something you have to do. If you're repeating a statement that deep down you don't believe in, you're not going to convince your mind to change. Your conscious mind is powerful, and it can easily overrule any affirmation that you try to feed it if you don't believe in it. Try to tell yourself —I am rich ‖ but the little voice in your head says, —No, you're not ‖ is not going to result in any positive change in your life or your mindset. You could repeat the same affirmation a thousand times a day, and it's still not going to do you any good.

The subconscious mind is a mix of repetition and emotion, but the thing is, you need to feed your mind with statements it can accept. That's how you get it to change.

How To Overcome Lack Of Self-Esteem

Thanks to its ability to be altered and shaped to be an effective tool for nearly anybody, this exercise and those who strongly support its benefits can easily claim to work best for anyone willing to give it a try. Those who have been searching for a way to understand themselves better and learn about where their personal restrictions come from will also find this exercise to be a powerful tool. Mainly, anyone who is hoping to expand their self-awareness and be honest with themselves about points of weakness they fear or try to ignore will find this exercise to be not only helpful and informational but illuminating and even may serve as a source of inspiration for those who have been trying to get motivated into self-improvement for some time without success.

STRATEGY 7

LEARN TO THINK LIKE AN OPTIMIST

There are different ways of defining how to think like an optimist. What a simple life is to you can mean a totally different thing to another person. An optimistic life means avoiding wasting your valuable time on things that are not important. As such, you value creating time for people and experiences that add meaning to your life.

Evaluate Your Time Usage

It is also crucial that you evaluate how you spend your time. Monitor how you use your time from the time you wake up to the end of the day. Create a list of the things that you often prioritize and those that usually distract you. By doing this frequently, you will identify things that only consume time and that are not important to you. In other words, you can redesign your day and work productively towards achieving your daily goals.

Learn to Say No

A fundamental habit that you ought to develop as you try to simplify your life is to learn to say no. Indeed, it is never easy to say no to your friends and colleagues at work. Unfortunately, this creates a situation where your to-do list will always be packed. What you should understand is that other people will be completing their tasks because you are helping them do what needs to be done on their to-do lists. On your end, you will have a lot pending. This is because you chose to accept extra tasks without putting yourself first. Therefore, it's never a bad thing to say no when you are doing it for the right reasons.

Plan Your Meals Wisely

Living a simple life also means that you should plan what you eat. Eating is part of your daily routine. This is something that you do throughout the day as long as you feel hungry. Accordingly, planning for your meals shouldn't be neglected. Make it a priority on your to-do list. Don't waste your time every day trying to figure out what you will be having for lunch or dinner. Just plan it. The good news is that doing this increases the likelihood of eating healthy foods that contribute to a productive lifestyle.

Address Your Debts

Oftentimes, people choose to ignore the debts that they have with the hopes that it will help them stop worrying. This doesn't help since you will only procrastinate the decision to pay your debts. Come up with a plan of how you will pay off your debts. Financially, it will help you make better decisions and open doors for business opportunities.

A simple life doesn't have to be something that is beyond your reach. It's all about identifying the things that are of great importance to you and prioritizing them. This creates time for you to enjoy with family and friends. So, live a simple life by keeping in mind the tips discussed in this chapter.

How do you know that you are an overthinker? There are signs that will indicate to you that you are thinking too much. For instance, if you find yourself over-analyzing things, then you are likely an overthinker. Sometimes life is just as simple as we perceive it to be. However, we make it difficult by thinking about it too much. When you meet someone for the first time, you might be overly judgmental as a result of thinking too much about how they are behaving. Avoid this by perceiving things as they are. In addition, if you find it difficult to let go of your past, then this is another clear sign that you are an overthinker. What happened in the past has nothing to do with your future. In fact, it only threatens your future since it holds you captive and prevents you from realizing your dreams.

As you go through your daily life, you should always remember that what you think about is what you become. This is the main reason why overthinking is tied to anxiety, stress, and negative thinking. Based on the law of attraction, you attract what you want in your life through your thoughts and emotions. Consequently, if you are always worrying about your future, then you will prevent yourself from truly being happy with the life you're living now. Similarly, thinking negatively about how your life doesn't help to save you from the situation. Sure, you might be going through a tough time. However, this doesn't mean that you should dwell on the negative. You should strive to find good in everything you go through in life. For instance, if you are going through a difficult time, consider this as a lesson worth going through. Life without challenges can be boring and risky at the same time. This is because you will be unlikely to learn and grow. As such, it is imperative that you embrace the notion of positive thinking since your life is dependent on how you think.

Get Rid of Toxic People

It will be daunting to live a simple life when you're surrounded by toxic people. These are people who never seem to add value to your life in any way. The worst thing is that they drain energy from you as they always think negatively. Also, they are the people that push you around to help them without stopping to help you.

Sure, some of these individuals are your best friends because there is a lot that you have been through with them. However, a keen eye on your relationship with them will reveal the fact that there is nothing you benefit from being friends with them. So, the best thing you can and should do is to eliminate them from your life. This might sound harsh. But the reality is that you will be doing yourself a favor by opening doors for more fruitful relationships.

Anger Management

Just like all other basic emotions, anger is designed to convey a specific message to us. That message could be our disapproval of something that has happened or something that someone has done. However, if our first response when angry is to vent or become raging mad, then the message gets lost in translation. For this reason, a calm mind and level-head are essential when dealing with anger. Being in a calm state of mind allows you to take a step back and objectively evaluate your anger from the point of reason. It also allows you to acknowledge your feelings and validate them without letting them control you.

Keeping calm when angry, however, is easier said than done. It takes a lot of practice, patience, and maturity to keep yourself from acting out of character when something that triggers rage in us happens. If someone offends you, it is much easier to revenge. In a way, we derive some pleasure from causing suffering to perceived opponents when we feel like they have wronged us. In reality, however, these solutions are illusory, since they do not deal with the real issues and cause of our anger. In fact, they can be more detrimental to us and our relationships in the long run. In light of this, we must find healthier ways to control our anger, even when we feel justified in it.

So, what is anger management, and what does it entail? Essentially, anger management is the process of identifying signs that you are becoming angry or frustrated and taking the necessary steps to calm yourself down in order to deal with your anger more productively. Many people have the misconception that anger management is meant to keep you from feeling angry. Others even think that it is designed to help them suppress feelings. Both of these are poor understandings of the role of anger management. Like we found out earlier, anger is a universal human emotion that all living humans experience at some point in their lives. Also, we already saw why suppressing anger is counterproductive as a long term strategy to manage anger.

The role of anger management is to help you become better at identifying signs that you are becoming frustrated and equip you with the necessary skills to keep your anger under control. A lot of literature has been written about anger and how to deal with it more effectively. One can, therefore, learn the right skills for dealing with frustration from reading books such as this one. However, the most common way through which people learn anger management is by attending an anger management class or therapy with a counselor.

You will get to learn how to identify the warning signs when you get frustrated, and how you can effectively calm yourself down in order to approach your anger from the point of strength.

You may be wondering to yourself right now, " How do I know if I need anger management classes?" Here are some of the signs that you may need to attend anger management classes in order to keep them in control.

You Constantly Feel Like You Need to Suppress Your Anger

While expressing your anger through fits of rage is not the appropriate response for anger, hiding your anger is not a healthy way of coping either. If you constantly feel like you need to bottle up your anger, this may point to a lack of proper coping strategy. It may also be that you are afraid of being vulnerable with other people and showing them your true feelings.

Vulnerability is very important in any relationship, as it helps to build trust among individuals. Refusal to be open about one's feelings usually leads to isolation, fear, and distrust. These are not only weak foundations on which to build a relationship, but they can also trigger more feelings of anger and frustration. It is, therefore, essential to take it upon yourself to learn the right coping strategies instead of hiding your feelings of rage.

You Always Focus on Negative Experiences

Granted, life is very challenging, and everyone will experience negativity in their lives at some point. However, it is important not to allow the bad things that happen in our lives to rid us of our joy and vitality. If you constantly focus only on the negative experiences in your life, you get distracted from actually living your life to the fullest potential. You may also find it a lot harder to appreciate the simple pleasures of everyday living, such as having a comfortable roof over your head, and people who love you. You, therefore, need to learn the right coping strategies when angry in order to prevent your anger from becoming habitual.

You Constantly Struggle with Feelings of Hostility and Irritation

If you constantly struggle with uncomfortable feelings of irritation and hostility towards others, then you definitely need to learn anger management skills. While life is not perfect every day, there are many things that make it worth the experience. If you are perennially irritated by the state of affairs in your life, this may point too deep-seated anger issues that need to be resolved as soon as possible.

You Constantly Find Yourself in Arguments which Further Trigger Your Anger

There are many instances in life when you will find yourself justifiably angry at someone for something they did. However, if you always find yourself in heated confrontations with people, this could be a sign of an underlying anger problem. It could also simply be a sign that the strategies you use to deal with your anger are ineffective. Perhaps your first response when angry is to blame the other person or throw a temper tantrum. Maybe you even find yourself engaging in abusive exchanges with the objects of your frustration. All of these strategies of coping with anger are very inappropriate since they only trigger more angry reactions from you. It is important instead to find a way of calming yourself down enough to deal with the issue with an objective mind.

You Engage in Physical Violence when Angry

While anger is a very normal reaction which may provoke feelings of aggression, using violence to deal with anger is very inappropriate. As a matter of fact, physically abusive responses when angry can be very damaging to your health, reputation as well as relationships. It can also lead to very serious legal consequences, such as getting sued or imprisoned for abuse. If you find yourself prone to committing acts of violence when angry, you should seek professional help immediately. Through counseling and attending anger management classes, you can break this cycle of poor anger management and learn to express your frustration in healthier ways that do not involve the use of violence.

You Manifest Out-of-Control Behavior when Angry

Perhaps you are not outrightly violent towards other people when angry. However, you may have a tendency to smash or break things when angry. This is still not an appropriate response or strategy to deal with anger and frustration. This type of behavior fails to address the real cause of the anger, and only reinforces the idea that showing aggression is going to make the anger go away. The truth is that it doesn't work. The only effective way of dealing with anger is by getting to the root cause and harnessing the emotion in positive ways.

You Avoid Certain Situations Because of Fear of Getting Angry

Another tell-tale sign that you need lessons in anger management is you find yourself constantly avoiding scenarios that may trigger your anger. Perhaps you don't like going to parties with your spouse because they always leave you alone to chat with the other people. Or maybe, you avoid talking to one of your close friends because you feel they are too judgmental.

Whichever the case, the temptation to avoid any scenario that may trigger your anger can be too strong to resist. However, opting out of certain situations due to fear of getting frustrated is not an effective way of dealing with your anger. For one, it shifts the responsibility to the other person, thereby diminishing your power to take responsibility for your emotions. It also only covers up pent up frustration, which continues to simmer slowly without your awareness. This can eventually erupt in very damaging ways, both to you and your relationships.

Anger management classes are typically designed to help people develop the skills to notice when they are getting angry and take the necessary steps to deal with the emotion appropriately. Usually, the classes are conducted as one-on-one sessions or group sessions with a counselor or therapist. Depending on your needs, the anger management program may take a few days, weeks, or even months in some cases. It is, therefore, essential for you to be patient and consider the whole experience as a learning process.

When you first begin attending anger management classes, the first thing you will learn is how to identify stressors and triggers of anger. By identifying the early warning signs of anger, you can begin to understand its causes and figure out how to control it. Stressors are typically those things that cause frustration in your life and trigger pent up anger. These may include frustration with a child who behaves poorly, financial problems, or coworkers who constantly gossip about you.

Apart from identifying the triggers, anger management classes will help teach you how to pick up on symptoms of anger. As we found out earlier, physiological symptoms of anger vary between individuals. You may, therefore, not manifest the same symptoms as someone else when angry. While one person may experience an increased heart rate and sweat when angry, another person may feel a tight-knot in their stomach when upset. Anger management classes will help you identify the physical symptoms of anger as they present uniquely in your body.

Beginner's anger management is also meant to help you recognize the signs that your anger is on the rise. Perhaps you may feel like you want to yell at the perceived object of your anger, or you feel the need to keep quiet in order to avoid a heated confrontation. Being aware of the physical reactions happening in your body will allow you to take a step back and carefully evaluate your anger before proceeding with an appropriate response.

7. Self-Healing

Guided Meditation For Self-Healing

Our unconscious mind is the determinant of all of our activities; it is a vast reservoir of information and knowledge. Yet this level of mind has some limitations. Visualization is a wonderful technique for healing the mind and body from the painful thoughts and physical symptoms of anxiety. Read the script properly and memorize the steps before practicing this meditation.

If you are lying, keep your legs apart, hands a little away from the torso with palms facing the ceiling.

Journeying into Healing

You are now ready to take the journey into the world of healing. Take a slow deep breath through your nose as you count from one to five under your breath.

- Breathe in (count from one to five)

- Exhale (count from one to eight)

- Now breathe normally and follow your breath. Pay complete attention to your breath. Feel your chest expand and contract with every breath. Imagine your mind is slowing down with each breath. Keep breathing.

- Pay attention to your body from head to toe. Feel the tightness and tension leaving your muscles and they are becoming limp.

- Feel that your whole body is getting heavier with each in-breath.

- Feel the gravity. Keep breathing

- You are getting so heavy…. you are unable to move…

- Feel the gravitational pull is increasing with every breath. Your body is turning into stone.

- Keep breathing.

- Feel the gravity is getting stronger, feel the pull

- The pull has become so strong that the body of stone is beginning to crack and crumble with every breath.

- Feel your whole body: your head, torso, hands, legs are cracking and crumbling.

- Keep breathing.

- Now feel your whole body is disintegrating gradually with every in-breath.

- Your body is turning into dust. Keep breathing.

- Your body has turned into a pile of dust.

- Now imagine a strong wind is blowing and lifting your body of dust.

- Your body of dust is being scattered.

- You are no longer in your body.

- You are now your consciousness.

- Feel that you are boundless.

- Omnipresent

- You are feeling peace, tranquility.

- Now imagine you are in a dream road that leads towards your home. Decorate the road the way you want, it is your very own world…this is the place where you feel most safe and secure.

- You are walking slowly in bare feet enjoying the serene beauty laying either side of the way. Feel the ground beneath your feet or the soft grass. Hear the birds singing and smell the sweet aroma of the wonderfully beautiful flowers. Enjoy the beauty as you are heading towards your dream home.

- Your home is a place where you feel most comfortable. Create your home the way you want.

- You can imagine your home by a fountain, by the sea or in a beautiful forest.

- You are not in a rush. Take time to enjoy the surroundings and when you are done, step into your house.

- Feel the soft carpet underneath your feet.

- Add whatever features you want in your home. You can add a library, a healing room, a command center; add as many rooms as you want. Imagine as vividly as you can then add color, texture, smell, and sounds.

- Step into your healing center, bring color, smell, texture. Imagine as vividly as you can.

- Now walk into the healing center. In your healing center, you have all the healing tools from ancient to modern at your disposal, to cure any kind of ailments.

- Now take a deep slow breath and exhale. Spend more time in exhaling. Again, inhale deeply and exhale slowly. One more time—breathe in and breathe out.

- Look at yourself in the mirror and think about your child-self. Think back to when you were a little kid.

- Now allow your inner-child to recall the most painful incident that you suffered as a child. It could be an event that involved actual or threatened death or serious injury, torture or abuse, no matter how distressing it is, allow your inner child to bring it to the forefront of your memory. If you can't get anything specific, then calmly say to your inner child:

My dear child, it hurts me to see you suffer.

I love you. Allow me to take your pain away.

Please allow me to heal the wound you hold inside you.

- If the wound has been identified (specific painful incident or general distressing feeling), look yourself in the mirror and stare deep into your eyes. Hold your gaze. Don't look away. Now say aloud what this wound is. If your wound is an intrusive humiliating memory, say it loud. Is it a memory of messing up a presentation or being humiliated by the teacher in front of the class in junior high? Say it loud. Repeat it… and keep repeating it until you feel your inner child's pain and fear deep in your heart, in your stomach and everywhere in your body.

- Take time to get fully connected with the inner child's truth.

- Now take a moment to look at your inner child's face. Look closely at the child's sad face (at the mirror), hear its voice, feel its pain. Now keep silent and allow your inner-child to talk. There are buried pain and unresolved conflicts deep inside, and it must be released.

- Now go to your inner-child as an adult (it is important that you imagine yourself as the inner-child and as an adult separately) with a smile on your face (because smiling will make your inner child feel comfortable with you).

- Respect the inner child and show respect to their concerns. Make sure to treat your inner child as a child. Reassure and show love.

- Envision yourself hugging your inner child. Feel the warmth and let the child feel safe and secure in your arms. The goal is to get the inner-child to cry and grieve. It will only happen when you gain their trust.

- Now show your inner child how your adult self perceives that incident. Tell it the truth; give it a reason to harmonize with you as an adult. Tell your inner child, —I will always be here to love and protect you, whenever you need me. ‖ Say it a few m oretimes.

- Now, walk up to the healing machine that looks like a star-trek healing device.

- Get on the healing device and lie down comfortably. Close your eyes - lids are gradually closing.

- The healing process has been initiated. Gradually you are getting relieved of all your discomforts and all your sorrows are melting away - all your inner-conflicts are disappearing. Feel that you are recovering from all your agonies.

- Keep breathing and take time to feel.

- The healing process is complete and your lids are slowly opening.

- Gently get off the device and slowly step outside the healing center.

- Breathe in and out.

- Take a slow walk along the road that leads towards the real world.

- Take a deep breath. You've reached the end of the road and an inter-dimensional doorway has appeared.

- Step into the doorway.

- Now imagine a gentle breeze is blowing.

- Breathe in. Your body is being created out of dust. Breathe out.

- Your body of dust is consolidating and turning into a body of rock. Breathe in. Your body of rock is gradually becoming alive. Breathe in. Breathe out.

- Now you are ready to wake up. Softly open your eyes.

- Stretch your hands and legs…

You are feeling fresh and wide-awake. Remember you have access to this feeling anytime you want.

Overcoming Death Anxiety

Have you noticed that all your irrational fears, whether it's a fear of having a panic attack or fear of being humiliated, can be traced back to one, truly specific fear - —the fear of death? ‖ Every fear is a fear of death in disguise. Your fears may have their own diagnoses, may be dealt with differently, but at the end of the day, it's all the same fear.

Our next exercise is devoted to getting over the fear of death in panic disorder.

- Get yourself comfortable. Sit on a chair or a cushion or the floor. Close your eyes. Breathe normally and allow your mind to settle in the present moment. This meditation can last as long as thirty minutes or as few as five minutes. Breathe naturally and become aware that every breath you take brings you closer to your last breath. You may plan lots of things for the coming days, and years, but nothing in human life is certain, except death.

- Imagine the people of the past—kings, rulers, philosophers, scientists, singers, and your forefathers. Those people were once alive— they enjoyed riches and fame, they wrote, they sang, loved, they fought, they suffered and finally they died.

- No one was born and never died. No matter how great or powerful a person may be, his or her life must meet its end in death. The same is true for all living things. The science of medicine may hope to find a cure for all diseases, but no science will ever find a cure for death.

- Picture in your mind the people you know who have already died. Then visualize the people you love and care about. They all will die one day—and so will you.

- More than seven billion people are now living on earth—but one hundred years from now, they will all disappear, except for the few who are very young. You too will be dead. Contemplate this fact and embrace the feeling that arises with this realization.

- Now think about the fragility of the human body. This body is vulnerable— the disease can strike, or an accident can happen and within seconds it can turn from being healthy and active to being weak and dying. Remember the times when you were ill. Become aware of the fact that sickness can occur again and can even progress until death. The body is impermanent. It will lose its beauty, it will decay and it will die.

- Now picture yourself lying on your deathbed. You're going to leave your loved ones behind—they are your strongest attachments. But you have to let go of your attachments.

- Now imagine your own funeral. Imagine yourself in an open casket. Feel the temperature. Smell the fresh flowers. Observe your surroundings. Hear the soft music in the background.

- Now let go of your body. Let it be there as an object that is no longer yours. Imagine being completely alone…. go to the limit of your feeling.

- Now take a good look around the room. What do you see?

- Perhaps you can see your family, your loved ones, relatives, friends, colleagues, and neighbors. Listen to what they are saying about you. What is your partner saying, your parents, your kids, someone you've met one time or another? Listen closely to each of them. What you hear reflects how you want the people that you care about you to remember.

- Now keep imagining the situation, while remembering the comments in your head. Perhaps one of them said, —He always looked nervous. I wish he'd done more with his life. ‖ 0 r —H e w as avery quiet gentle soul. ‖

- Stay with this image for a while. Now gently come back to your living body. Your life is not over yet. You still have time to be the person you want. Bring the feeling of love and respect for your living body. Allow this feeling to spread inside you, throughout your entire organism. Then allow it to spread out around you and everything.

Changing Your Lifestyle To Regain Control Of Your Life

Diet and Anxiety Attacks

Much of what we eat today is laced with chemicals that can add to the burden on our already weary bodies. Few people eat healthy anymore and many are living on junk food that is laced with ingredients that are not good for us. The old saying that —you are what you eat ‖ rings true when it comes to diet and anxiety attacks. Some of the culprits that can be found in our diet as well as our habits include caffeine, nicotine, sugar and fatty foods. These can all play a role in keeping us in our anxious state.

Nicotine

Smokers will often say that smoking —calms them down. ‖ The iiony is that just the opposite is true. Nicotine that is contained in cigarette smoke will actually make you feel more anxious. Nicotine constricts the blood vessels and aids in anxiety instead of preventing it. If you are smoking to —calm your nerves ‖ you are doing yourself more harm than good. Aside from the other problems that smoking causes, it also raises your heart rate.

When you quit smoking, you may find that the withdrawal from nicotine raises your anxiety level, preventing you from quitting. The withdrawal from nicotine is very bad. In fact, many doctors believe that it is one of the worst withdrawals to have to endure. Many in the medical community will state that nicotine is even more addictive than heroin.

The physical effects of nicotine in your system last for 72 hours. Once you get past Day 3 without cigarettes, your physical craving for nicotine is gone. The mental craving might still be there - in fact, it may never even leave you - but the physical withdrawal symptoms are over.

Many doctors will prescribe anti-depressants such as Wellbutrin for people who are planning to quit smoking. This takes some of the edge off of the quitting process and some state that it aids in quitting.

If you smoke, you are only adding to your anxiety. On top of every other bad thing that it causes, smoking also raises your heart rate, constricts your blood vessels and aids in anxiety. If you have anxiety attacks, you should not smoke.

Caffeine

How much caffeine do you take in on a daily basis? For some people, cigarettes and black coffee are the ideal breakfast combo. If you are following in this path, you might want to lay off the caffeine. If you enjoy a cup of coffee, you can do so just as well with decaffeinated coffee.

Caffeine makes you very jittery and can help along your anxiety. While it is common to have a cup of coffee in the morning, having two or three cups can aid in your anxiety. The truth of the matter is that caffeine is really not good for you and promotes a false sense of awareness.

If you have been suffering from anxiety attacks, take a look at your daily caffeine absorption. If you are drinking coffee, soda, or tea all day long, you are aiding with your problem. Caffeine will make you feel tenser than ever. If you are trying to drive cross country, you might want to keep yourself up with Java, but it is a false sense of awareness. People who come down off of a caffeine high usually crash hard.

Caffeine, like nicotine, is not good for you. Take a look at how much caffeine you are taking in with regard to what you drink. If you are overweight, a good deal of the reason can be because of what you are drinking instead of what you are eating. Many people who do not like coffee will state that they like soda or tea instead. The truth of the matter is that there is caffeine in almost all sodas as well as tea and cocoa. Coca-Cola has about as much caffeine as a cup of coffee.

If you drink coffee, limit it to drinking in the morning and to one cup per day. If you want to go decaffeinated, do that, but be advised that it still contains some caffeine. Do not delude yourself into thinking that decaffeinated means —no caffeine. ‖ It just means that there is a lot less caffeine in the drink than normal.

Chocolate also contains caffeine. While studies show that small portions of dark chocolate are good for your heart, you should not take chocolate at night. It may end up making you more on edge and will not have a calming effect.

If you take over the counter pain medications, take them for PM instead of regular medications, and take them sparingly. This is because many of the over the counter pain relief medications contain caffeine. If you want to help yourself eliminate some of the stress from your life and overcome or prevent anxiety and panic attacks, you will lay off the caffeine. That means be aware of how much caffeine there is in coffee, tea and soda and absorb it accordingly. If you can cut it out from your diet altogether, all the better.

The withdrawal from caffeine usually consists of a headache. You may have a headache for a day, but once you get over it, the caffeine will have left your system.

Sugar

Sure, we'll all take in sugar, but too much of this sweet thing can end up helping our anxiety along. Take a look at the simple carbohydrates you are eating and try to cut some of them out. Simple carbohydrates consist of cakes, cookies, candy, and other sweets. These offer no nutritional value and pack on the pounds. Packing on the pounds is also hard on anyone who is prone to anxiety.

Start fighting your condition by taking control of what you eat. This includes the amount of sugar intake. You get as many refined sugars in your everyday meals that you do not have to add to it by consuming too much sugar.

If you take in a lot of sugar, you may end up getting Type II Diabetes, which is pretty much at epidemic proportions in the United States. Or you might end up getting hypoglycemia. Hypoglycemia is when your sugar levels drop below normal levels. When this happens, you may feel something akin to that of a panic attack. Your heart will race, your skin will feel clammy and you may even faint.

Anyone who suffers from panic or anxiety attacks should consider cutting the sugar out of their diet. We get plenty of sugar in our everyday diets as it is that we do not have to add to it by eating things that offer no nutritional value. Refined sugars are everywhere. If you are finding that your anxiety attacks are at their worst after you have eaten, it could be because you are taking in too much sugar.

Fatty Foods

Fat is very common in fast foods and many of the other foods that we eat. Studies suggest that this is not good for our health and can contribute to depression and anxiety. People who are overweight are more inclined to suffer from anxiety and depression than those who are of average weight.

One way that you can eliminate fat from your diet is to cut out the fast food. If you are living off of hamburgers, fried chicken, fries and other junk foods. While these foods are often thought of as —comfort foods, ‖ in reality, they do not comfort someone who is eating them. Fat foods do not help anyone who has anxiety. They only add to the problem and, in many cases, cause obesity.

If you are suffering from anxiety and depression, one of the things that you can do to help yourself is to eat a healthy diet. Lay off the simple carbohydrates and fats and stick to a diet that is rich in whole grains, fruits, and vegetables. Taking a multivitamin or a B-complex vitamin can help you with stress as well. Start incorporating more vitamins into your meals, reduce fat and sugars and eliminate caffeine. If you are smoking, stop.

In addition to what you eat, watch how you eat. Do you take time to chew your food thoroughly or are you eating in gulps? Many times, when we are under stress, we eat. When you eat food that is swallowed in chunks, you are not digesting the food properly and actually depriving yourself of nutrients that the food can give you. In addition to that, you are most likely overeating if you are not chewing your food properly. You are not only harming your digestive system, but you are causing yourself to lose nutrients and may be contributing to your anxiety attacks.

Take your time to eat your food by chewing it thoroughly before swallowing. Start making some changes in your diet right now to not only help you with regard to your anxiety, but your overall health.

You really are what you eat and if you are eating too much junk food and not getting enough nutrients, it is bound to make you feel bad. If you want to be healthier both physically and mentally, start eating a healthy diet that is full of nutrients and vitamins and chewing your food properly.

Another thing that you should do when you are watching your diet is to watch what you drink. Get rid of the caffeinated drinks and sodas and switch to water. By drinking 8 glasses of water each day, you will raise your metabolism and actually feel better. You should also increase your intake of fiber and limit your consumption of red meats, opting for fish instead.

Action Plans

Action Plan I – Dealing with Anxious Thoughts

Nothing impacts your thoughts as much as anxiety. Suddenly, the world comes to a standstill, and you begin to think that everyday things and situations may be threatening to you. The feeling that everything is going wrong and you will not be able to deal with the situation makes anxiety psychologically dangerous.

You may start finding normal situations, or situations that seemed normal to you the last time they occurred, potentially dangerous. For instance, having a cough may bother you and force you to think that you are suffering from some chronic disorder of which coughing is a symptom, or your child is 10 minutes from school may compel to think about all the wrong things that could have happened to him.

As a general rule, people with anxiety live under the constant fear that something is going wrong so much so that they may be dreadful to cope with. What they fear is not just the situation, but also the fact that they won't be able to manage them and remain calm and safe in it. This is a vicious circle of sorts. When you feel anxious, you are surrounded by thoughts of fear, thread, and avoidance. Moreover, when you consider a situation negative or threatening, you are likely to get anxious about it.

What you think directly impacts what you feel, and if you can curb your thoughts, your anxiety levels will automatically drop. Let us take the example of two ladies who are waiting for their children to come home from a party, late at night. Their children are out of a party and had promised to come back by 11 that night. The first lady begins to panic as the clock strikes 11, and every minute past that time her anxiety levels rise. To add to her misery, she begins to think about all the bad things that could have happened to her child, which adds up to the anxiety substantially.

The second lady also gets anxious to find out why her child is not back at 11. However, she remembers all the times when her child had promised to be back by a certain time and had arrived 10 minutes late, so her anxiety levels drop. In both the cases, the ladies got anxious, however, while the first lady increased her anxiety levels by thinking about things that escalated her worrying, the second lady thought of things that helped her manage her anxiety.

Suffice to say; thoughts have a significant impact on your overall anxiety levels. An increased anxiety level will translate into more serious physical symptoms. The best way to manage the scenario is to break the cycle of anxiety and thoughts by thinking from a positive and constructive perspective.

To help you manage anxious thoughts, you need to give yourself some time and follow the two-step exercise explained below.

1. The first step is to identify the thoughts that are making you anxious.

2. The second step is to replace these thoughts with alternative thoughts which are more constructive and realistic.

You cannot challenge anxiety unless you know the cause behind it. This is exactly the reason why identifying anxious thoughts is extremely important. With this said, it is equally important to state that this identification process will not be simple. Such thoughts are automatic and so quick in occurring that you don't even realize that something you thought just raised your anxiety levels. Fortunately, the effects of anxiety are such that you will know that you are anxious and applying reverse psychology to the cause is the only option that lies with you. As you practice, identifying such thoughts will get easier.

Typically, anxious thoughts that take the shape of —what if‖ and —I don t'think I can cope. ‖ If you have experienced an embarrassing situation lately or an incident that has had a grave impact on your mind, then reliving the incident in our mind may also be a cause of anxiety. The most challenging aspect of identifying anxious thoughts is that you are already anxious, and being able to control your mind at such time for an analysis of this degree may be tough.

Therefore, it is a good idea to have well-framed questions to ask yourself every single time you get anxious. For instance, as yourself:

- Why am I feeling this way?

- How did it start?

- Are all my assumptions actually true?

- Will this actually happen?

- How will this impact me, my life, and the people around me?

How to Start?

Prepare a Thought Record

As you perform this activity, be sure to record your thoughts and answers in a diary. This will help you analyze the situation with a calmer mind at a later time. In this way, you will be able to use the information gathered for managing anxiety for future instances even if you weren't able to help yourself at the time it occurred. This record sheet can also play an instrumental role in determining behavioral patterns and identifying underlying issues if any are present.

Determine the Realistic Thoughts from Anxious Thoughts

Once the identification process is complete, and you know how to do it at the time of anxiety, as well as analyze the pattern over a period, the next step is to determine if the thoughts are realistic. Most anxious thoughts are actually assumptions or exaggerated reactions to situations. Therefore, this step will help you get a realistic and objective viewpoint on the situation.

Moving forward, you must look for an alternative way of thinking about the situation. This is a daunting task, and you will need to practice this method a lot before you can be an expert on it. In the previous step, you had prepared a thoughts record. In this step, you may add two columns to the thought record, one each for evidence that supports your thought and the one that goes against it. Use these columns to create a new column, which gives an alternative and realistic thought for replacing the existing anxious thought.

Assessment

No method is effective unless it can help you reduce your anxiety levels. Therefore, before you sit down to write the record: assess your anxiety levels by rating it on a scale from 1 to 10; 1 being the least anxious and ten being the highest. Rate your anxiety levels after you have evaluated the alternative thought using the method illustrated here. This will help you know if the method is working for you.

Action Plan II – Dealing With Avoidance

When a situation makes you feel anxious, it is understandable and obvious that you will try to avoid the situation at any cost. This is, in actuality, a short-term solution to your problem. You will avoid the situation, and you will not have to face it. Therefore, for the moment, it is a good strategy to get rid of anxiety. However, when you talk about the long-term impact of anxiety, you will realize that such a behavior lessens your chances of being able to cope with anxiety in the future.

Let us take the example of an individual who fears social situations and avoids attending social gatherings. Her friends ask her out for coffee, but she makes an excuse. In other words, she avoids the situation. However, when her same friends ask her out again, she is likely to feel all the more anxious about meeting her friends because she had not met them from the last time, and she will have to explain declining another invitation.

In a way, the girl was anxious about being a part of a social gathering, so she avoided the situation. While this avoidance helped her manage the situation at that time, it did not make any substantial contribution in helping her face such situations that may encounter in the future, and the next time she is faced with such a situation she will feel anxious again. You need to break this cycle to manage your anxiety problem.

Obviously, not facing the issue will not help you in any way. You will have to face the situation and break the cycle. Feeling anxious is natural and fine, in some cases. You don't have to believe that there is something abnormal about the fact that you are feeling anxious. Moreover, once you face the situation, you will realize the anxiety levels have automatically gone down. This will also reduce the anxiety levels that you will experience the next time you face a similar situation.

Three Things You Can Do Towards Managing Avoidance

First, ever assume that you will be able to get rid of all your anxiety the first time you encounter an anxiety-provoking situation. It is a gradual process.

Secondly, in your attempts to manage anxiety, you must face an anxiety-provoking situation that is least anxiety-provoking.

Once you can face it, you will rise in confidence and will be in a much better position to face a greater anxiety-provoking situation that the last one. Lastly, it is a good idea to make a list of all the things that make you anxious. Although this activity will be anxiety-provoking and a lot of hard work for you, it can be a great way to deal with the situations when they face you.

CONCLUSION

Thank you for making it to the end. I hope this book has helped you to feel good and battle with depression, anxiety, and stress. Aside from being mindful when you interact with others, it is also important that you develop self-confidence when facing other situations, whether they are connected to social situations or not. As I end this book, here are some tips on how to raise your self confidence in order to feel good, in everything you do.

Never compare yourself with other people

Each person is unique in his/her own way. Therefore, it is not good to compare yourself with others. Instead of looking at another person and telling yourself that they are better than you when it comes to the interview or on a date, you should just focus on what you think you have that others don't. You may not have enough knowledge on a particular topic, but you may have a great sense of humor. Focus on what you have, not on the qualities that you don't have. By doing so, you will be more encouraged to engage in a social situation and let other people see what you can give to them.

Constantly affirm yourself

Declaring that something is true can greatly affect any person's mindset and actions. For those with social anxiety, affirmations such as —I am an employee of this company after the interview ‖ will give them the confidence to engage on the activity and approach it positively. This in turn will help them modify their actions so that the affirmation will come true.

Set your goals and start accomplishing them one small step at a time

Self-confidence continues to increase whenever you achieve something important. Therefore, you need to set a goal based on what you think is necessary in your life and for your improvement. Make a list of these goals, and make a plan as to how these goals can be accomplished.

But in order for you to achieve your long-term goals, you will need to break it down into smaller objectives that, when combined, are necessary to accomplish the bigger picture. By accomplishing these small tasks one after another, you will become more motivated to continue with your actions (since results are easily seen). This also builds confidence, as you are able to prove to yourself that you can accomplish different tasks.

Develop contingency plans

Situations do not always go your way. Aside from planning how you can become successful on any task, you should also have a plan as to what can be done if ever things go wrong. Not only will you be able to remedy the situation, it will also increase your confidence (since you were able to deal with a situation that somehow diverted from your plan).

By building on your self-confidence, you will be able to take on other things aside from interaction (such as opportunities arising from them). By engaging in these things, it will be easier for you to attain success in whatever it is that you want to accomplish.

I hope you have learned something!

INDEX

addictive relationship, 57, 58, 59, 60

addictive relationships, 57, 58, 59

anger, 13, 26, 43, 44, 54, 69, 70, 71, 72

anxiety, 12, 15, 16, 17, 18, 19, 20, 21, 22, 23, 24, 25, 26, 27, 28, 30, 31, 36, 46, 49, 50, 54, 68, 73, 78, 79, 80, 81, 82, 83, 84, 85, 87

change, 1, 3, 6, 8, 16, 17, 19, 21, 30, 31, 45, 65, 66

depression, 3, 4, 5, 6, 7, 8, 9, 10, 11, 12, 13, 19, 26, 27, 40, 44, 46, 54, 81, 87

Depression, 3, 4, 8, 13, 26

enjoy, 1, 4, 13, 23, 68, 74, 79

fear, 8, 15, 16, 17, 18, 23, 27, 29, 37, 44, 49, 54, 66, 70, 71, 75, 77, 82

gratitude, 1, 2

happy, 1, 8, 13, 30, 32, 33, 40, 58, 60, 63, 66, 68

illness, 3, 26, 28, 29

mental, 3, 9, 11, 12, 16, 21, 28, 30, 33, 35, 36, 37, 38, 39, 40, 44, 45, 47, 48, 63, 79

mood, 3, 4, 9, 10, 11, 45, 55

negative thoughts, 5, 40, 41, 43, 44, 45, 50, 52, 53, 54, 55, 56

Negative thoughts, 20, 43

pleasure, 3, 33, 44, 69

sadness, 3, 11, 44, 57, 60

self, 1, 3, 4, 5, 6, 35, 36, 38, 47, 50, 52, 55, 56, 58, 61, 62, 63, 64, 65, 66, 75, 76, 87, 88 self-esteem, 61, 62, 63, 64

stress, 8, 10, 15, 24, 25, 26, 27, 28, 29, 30, 31, 32, 33, 34, 36, 46, 48, 50, 54, 63, 65, 68, 80, 81, 87

symptoms, 3, 8, 16, 18, 27, 30, 72, 73, 79, 82

THERAPY, i

worry, 16, 17, 20, 21, 22, 23, 24, 27, 36, 49, 55

CPSIA information can be obtained
at www.ICGtesting.com
Printed in the USA
BVHW050100020321
601387BV00013B/1294